THE ULTIMATE
OAKLAND ATHLETICS
TRIVIA BOOK

A Collection of Amazing Trivia Quizzes
and Fun Facts for Die-Hard A's Fans!

Ray Walker

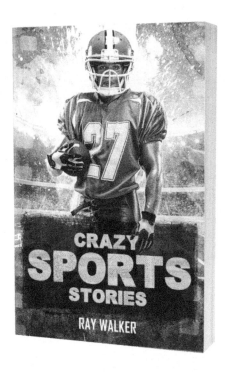

CONTENTS

INTRODUCTION

The Oakland Athletics were established in 1901. They were previously known as the Philadelphia Athletics and the Kansas City Athletics. No matter their name or location, they have consistently proven themselves to be a team that fights hard and is a force to be reckoned with in MLB.

They currently hold nine World Series championships, which they won in 1910, 1911, 1913, 1929, 1930, 1972, 1973, 1974, and 1989. They have won 15 American League pennants, 17 AL West Division titles, and 4 wild card berths. They are very often a threat in the American League West Division, having last won it in 2020. They made their most recent World Series appearance in 1990.

The Oakland Athletics have retired the numbers of Reggie Jackson, Rickey Henderson, Catfish Hunter, Rollie Fingers, Dennis Eckersley, and, of course, Jackie Robinson.

The Oakland Athletics' current home is the Oakland Coliseum, which opened in 1966. They play in one of the most difficult divisions in baseball, the American League West, alongside the Los Angeles Angels, Seattle Mariners, Texas Rangers, and Houston Astros.

The thing about baseball is that it is a lot like life. There are good times and bad times, good days and bad days, but you have to do your absolute best to never give up. The Oakland A's have proven that they refuse to give up and that they will do anything they need to do to bring a championship to the town. Winning is more than possible when you have a storied past like the Oakland Athletics. They have so much captivating history and so many undeniable player legacies to be profoundly proud of.

With such a storied team past that goes back generations, you're probably already very knowledgeable as the die-hard Green and Gold fan that you are. Let's test that knowledge to see if you truly are the world's biggest A's fan.

CHAPTER 1:

ORIGINS & HISTORY

QUIZ TIME!

1. Which of the following team names did the Oakland A's franchise once go by?

   a. Philadelphia Athletics
   b. Kansas City Athletics
   c. San Diego Athletics
   d. Both A and B

2. In what year was the franchise established?

   a. 1891
   b. 1901
   c. 1921
   d. 1951

3. The Oakland Athletics' current home stadium is RingCentral Coliseum.

   a. True
   b. False

4. Which division do the Oakland A's play in?

a. American League West

b. National League West

c. American League Central

d. National League Central

5. The Oakland A's have never won a wild card berth.

   a. True

   b. False

6. How many American League pennants have the Oakland Athletics franchise won (as of the 2020 season)?

   a. 5

   b. 10

   c. 15

   d. 20

7. Who is the current principal owner of the Oakland A's?

   a. Larry Dolan

   b. Robert Nutting

   c. Arturo Moreno

   d. John Fisher

8. Who is the winningest manager in Oakland A's history (as of the 2020 season)?

   a. Billy Martin

   b. Bob Melvin

   c. Connie Mack

   d. Tony LaRussa

9. What is the name of the Oakland Athletics Triple-A Team and where is it located?

a. Albuquerque Isotopes

b. Jacksonville Jumbo Shrimp

c. Toledo Mud Hens

d. Las Vegas Aviators

10. Who was the first manager of the franchise?

a. Earle Mack

b. Connie Mack

c. Harry Craft

d. Hank Bauer

11. The Oakland A's were members of the National League West from 1969 through 1993.

a. True

b. False

12. What is the name of the Oakland Athletics' current spring training home stadium?

a. Goodyear Ballpark

b. Hohokam Stadium

c. Salt River Fields

d. Sloan Park

13. How many appearances has the Oakland A's franchise made in the MLB playoffs (as of the end of the 2020 season)?

a. 9

b. 19

c. 29

d. 39

14. How many World Series titles have the Oakland A's won (as of the 2020 season)?

    a. 6
    b. 7
    c. 8
    d. 9

15. The Oakland Athletics' current manager is Bob Melvin.

    a. True
    b. False

16. What was the franchise's first home stadium?

    a. Shibe Park
    b. Columbia Park
    c. Oakland-Alameda County Coliseum
    d. Municipal Park

17. Who is the current general manager of the Oakland A's?

    a. Mike Rizzo
    b. Sam Fuld
    c. David Forst
    d. Jerry Dipoto

18. How many American League West Division titles have the Oakland A's won (as of the end of the 2020 season)?

    a. 11
    b. 13
    c. 15
    d. 17

19. Dave Kaval is the current president of the Oakland A's.

    a. True

    b. False

20. Billy Beane is the current president of baseball operations of the Oakland A's.

    a. True

    b. False

QUIZ ANSWERS

1. D – Both A and B

2. B – 1901

3. A- True

4. A – American League West

5. B – False, 4 (2001, 2014, 2018, 2019)

6. C – 15

7. D – John Fisher

8. C – Connie Mack

9. D – Las Vegas Aviators

10. B – Connie Mack

11. B – False, they have always been in the AL West.

12. B – Hohokam Stadium

13. C – 29

14. D – 9

15. A – True

16. B – Columbia Park

17. C – David Forst

18. D – 17

19. A – True

20. A – True

DID YOU KNOW?

1. The franchise has had 30 managers so far: Connie Mack, Earle Mack, Jimmy Dykes, Eddie Joost, Lou Boudreau, Harry Craft, Bob Elliott, Joe Gordon, Hank Bauer, Eddie Lopat, Mel McGaha, Haywood Sullivan, Alvin Dark, Luke Appling, Bob Kennedy, John McNamara, Dick Williams, Chuck Tanner, Jack McKeon, Bobby Winkles, Jim Marshall, Billy Martin, Steve Boros, Jackie Moore, Jeff Newman, Tony La Russa, Art Howe, Ken Macha, Bob Geren, and Bob Melvin.

2. The Oakland Athletics' current manager is Bob Melvin. He has been their manager since 2011. He was a catcher for the Detroit Tigers, San Francisco Giants, Baltimore Orioles, Kansas City Royals, Boston Red Sox, New York Yankees, and Chicago White Sox and he has coached for the Milwaukee Brewers, Detroit Tigers, and Arizona Diamondbacks. He has also had stints as manager of the Seattle Mariners and Arizona Diamondbacks. Melvin attended college at the University of California, Berkeley. He is currently the longest-tenured manager in the MLB with the same team.

3. Connie Mack is the Oakland Athletics' all-time winningest manager with a record of 3,582-3,814 (.484 W-L%). Connie Mack managed the Philadelphia Athletics from 1901 through 1950. He also managed the Pittsburgh

Pirates from 1894 through 1896. He was a 5x World Series champion with the A's and holds the records for most managerial games, wins, and losses in MLB history. He was inducted into the National Baseball Hall of Fame in 1937.

4. Billy Beane is the current president of baseball operations for the Oakland A's. He was the Athletics' general manager from 1998 to 2016. He was featured in the 2011 Oscar-nominated film, *Moneyball*, where he was portrayed by Brad Pitt. As a player, he had stints with the New York Mets, Minnesota Twins, A's, and Detroit Tigers.

5. The franchise has hosted three MLB All-Star Games so far: 1943 at Shibe Park, 1960 at Municipal Stadium, and 1987 at Oakland-Alameda County Coliseum.

6. The Oakland A's have had 13 no-hitters thrown in franchise history. Two of them were perfect games. The most recent no-hitter was thrown by Mike Fiers on May 7, 2019, against the Cincinnati Reds. The most recent perfect game was thrown by Dallas Braden on May 9, 2010, against the Tampa Bay Rays.

7. Dave Stewart is set to have his No. 34 retired by the Oakland Athletics. He was supposed to have his number retired in 2020 but it was postponed due to the COVID-19 pandemic.

8. The Oakland Athletics' Double-A team is the Midland RockHounds; High Single-A is the Lansing Lugnuts, and Low Single-A is the Stockton Ports.

9. The Oakland Athletics' current mascot is an elephant named "Stomper." You can find him at A's games driving around in his Chevron car and greeting fans in the stands. He wears the number "00" on his A's uniform.

10. The Oakland A's have retired five numbers so far in franchise history; six including Jackie Robinson's No. 42, which is retired league-wide. Numbers retired are Reggie Jackson's No. 9, Rickey Henderson's No. 24, Catfish Hunter's No. 27, Rollie Fingers' No. 34, and Dennis Eckersley's No. 43.

CHAPTER 2:

JERSEYS & NUMBERS

QUIZ TIME!

1. The A's have a tradition of wearing white cleats team-wide.

    a. True
    b. False

2. What are the Oakland Athletics' official team colors?

    a. Kelly green, lemon yellow, ivory white
    b. Forest green, Fort Knox gold, wedding gown white
    c. Kelly green, Fort Knox gold, wedding gown white
    d. Forest green, sunny yellow, ivory white

3. In 2000 and 2008, the Oakland A's wore black jerseys.

    a. True
    b. False

4. Which of the following numbers has NOT been retired by the Oakland A's (as of the end of the 2020 season)?

    a. 24
    b. 25

c. 34

d. 43

5. What number does Matt Chapman currently wear?

   a. 6

   b. 16

   c. 26

   d. 36

6. What number did Bert Campaneris wear during his time with the Oakland A's?

   a. 9

   b. 19

   c. 29

   d. 56

7. Eric Chavez wore the Nos. 30 and 3 during his time with the Oakland A's.

   a. True

   b. False

8. What number did Jose Canseco wear during his time with the Oakland A's?

   a. 3

   b. 11

   c. 22

   d. 33

9. Who is the only Oakland A's player to have ever worn the No. 75?

a. Sean Doolittle

b. Josh Outman

c. Ricardo Rincon

d. Barry Zito

10. No Oakland A's player has ever won the No. 0.

a. True

b. False

11. What number did Sal Bando wear as a member of the Oakland A's?

a. 6

b. 16

c. 26

d. 36

12. What number did Mark Ellis wear as a member of the Oakland A's?

a. 4

b. 14

c. 24

d. 34

13. Kurt Suzuki wore the Nos. 28, 6, 24, 8, and 22 during his time with the Oakland A's.

a. True

b. False

14. What number did Mark McGwire wear as a member of the Oakland A's?

a. 5

b. 15

c. 25

d. Both B and C

15. What number does Matt Olson currently wear as a member of the Oakland A's?

a. 8

b. 18

c. 28

d. None of the Above

16. What number did Catfish Hunter wear as a member of the Oakland A's?

a. 17

b. 27

c. 37

d. 47

17. During his time with the Oakland A's, Carney Lansford wore No. _____.

a. 4

b. 5

c. 14

d. Both A and B

18. What number did Reggie Jackson wear with the Oakland A's?

a. 9

b. 16

c. 31

d. Both A and C

19. What number did Dennis Eckersley wear as a member of the Oakland A's?

   a. 14

   b. 34

   c. 43

   d. 44

20. Dave Henderson wore No. 42 during his time with the Oakland A's.

   a. True

   b. False

QUIZ ANSWERS

1. A - True

2. C – Kelly green, Fort Knox gold, wedding gown white

3. A – True

4. B – 25

5. C – 26

6. B – 19

7. A – True

8. D – 33

9. D – Barry Zito

10. A – True

11. A – 6

12. B – 14

13. A – True

14. C – 25

15. C – 28

16. B – 27

17. D – Both A and B

18. D – Both A and C

19. C – 43

20. A – True

DID YOU KNOW?

1. The Oakland A's have retired six numbers overall so far in franchise history: Reggie Jackson (No. 9), Rickey Henderson (No. 24), Catfish Hunter (No. 27), Rollie Fingers (No. 34), Dennis Eckersley (No. 43), and Jackie Robinson (No. 42). Dave Stewart's No. 34 is also set to be retired by the team.

2. During his time with the Oakland A's, Ray Fosse wore No. 10.

3. Joe Rudi wore Nos. 15, 45, 8, and 26 during his time with the Kansas City/Oakland A's.

4. During his time with the Oakland A's, Terry Steinbach wore the No. 36.

5. During his time with the Oakland A's, Coco Crisp wore the No. 4.

6. During his time with the Oakland A's, Blue Moon Odom wore the No. 13.

7. Jackie Robinson's No. 42 has been retired by MLB as a whole. No A's or MLB player will ever wear No. 42 again. The Yankees' Mariano Rivera was the final player to wear it.

8. During his time with the Oakland A's, Vida Blue wore the Nos. 21, 28, 17, 35, and 14.

9. During his time with the Oakland A's, Nick Swisher wore the Nos. 25 and 33.

10. During his time with the Oakland A's, Gene Tenace wore the Nos. 24, 38, and 18.

CHAPTER 3:

MAN OF STEAL

QUIZ TIME!

1. What year was Rickey Henderson inducted into the National Baseball Hall of Fame?

   a. 2007
   b. 2008
   c. 2009
   d. 2010

2. Rickey Henderson played his entire 25-season MLB career with the Oakland A's.

   a. True
   b. False

3. Where was Rickey Henderson born?

   a. Oakland, CA
   b. San Diego, CA
   c. Peoria, IL
   d. Chicago, IL

4. When was Rickey Henderson born?

a. December 25, 1955

b. December 25, 1958

c. June 25, 1955

d. June 25, 1958

5. Rickey Henderson did NOT win a World Series championship during his time in the MLB.

   a. True

   b. False

6. How many MLB All-Star Games was Rickey Henderson named to during his 25-season MLB career?

   a. 5

   b. 10

   c. 20

   d. 25

7. Rickey Henderson holds the MLB record for stolen bases. How many did he steal?

   a. 1,106

   b. 1,206

   c. 1,306

   d. 1,406

8. Rickey Henderson was born "Rickey Nelson Henley.."

   a. True

   b. False

9. What is Rickey Henderson's career batting average?

   a. .269

   b. .279

c. .289

d. .299

10. How many times was Rickey Henderson named AL MVP?

    a. 0

    b. 1

    c. 2

    d. 3

11. How many Gold Glove Awards did Rickey Henderson win?

    a. 1

    b. 2

    c. 3

    d. 4

12. Rickey Henderson was named the 1989 ALCS MVP.

    a. True

    b. False

13. How many Silver Slugger Awards did Rickey Henderson win?

    a. 1

    b. 2

    c. 3

    d. 4

14. Rickey Henderson is a 12x American League stolen bases leader.

a. True

b. False

15. Rickey Henderson holds the MLB record for career runs scored with how many?

    a. 1,995

    b. 2,095

    c. 2,195

    d. 2,295

16. Rickey Henderson holds the MLB record for career leadoff home runs with how many?

    a. 71

    b. 81

    c. 91

    d. 101

17. Rickey Henderson holds the MLB single-season record for most stolen bases with 130.

    a. True

    b. False

18. How many home runs did Rickey Henderson hit?

    a. 267

    b. 277

    c. 287

    d. 297

19. How many hits did Rickey Henderson record?

    a. 2,895

    b. 2,955

c. 3,055

d. 3,155

20. Rickey Henderson's career WAR was 111. 2.

a. True

b. False

QUIZ ANSWERS

1. C – 2009

2. B – False (He played for the A's, New York Yankees, San Diego Padres, New York Mets, Boston Red Sox, Los Angeles Dodgers, Anaheim Angels, Seattle Mariners, and Toronto Blue Jays.}

3. D – Chicago, IL

4. B – December 25, 1958

5. B – False (1989, 1993)

6. B – 10

7. D – 1,406

8. A – True

9. B - .279

10. B – 1 (1990)

11. A – 1

12. A – True

13. C – 3

14. A – True

15. D – 2,295

16. B – 81

17. A - True

18. D – 297

19. C – 3,055

20. A – True

DID YOU KNOW?

1. Rickey Henderson was born in the back of an Oldsmobile on the way to the hospital. He joked, "I was already fast. I couldn't wait."

2. Rickey Henderson had 10,961 at-bats.

3. Rickey Henderson collected 1,115 RBI.

4. Rickey Henderson played 14 seasons with the Oakland A's in four different stints.

5. Rickey Henderson was named the American League Player of the Week five times and he was named the American League Player of the Month once.

6. Rickey Henderson's childhood dream was to play football for the Oakland Raiders but his mom persuaded him to pursue baseball instead. In high school, Rickey was an All-American running back with two 1,000 yard rushing seasons.

7. "If you could split him in two, you'd have two Hall of Famers." – Statistician Bill James on Rickey Henderson

8. Rickey Henderson broke Lou Brock's stolen base record on May 1, 1991, with his 939th stolen base.

9. "Today, I am the greatest of all time."

10. Rickey Henderson tends to talk in the third person and often refers to himself as "Rickey."

11. Rickey Henderson made his MLB debut in 1979 and played in his final MLB game in 2003.

CHAPTER 4:

CATCHY NICKNAMES

QUIZ TIME!

1. What nickname does Mark McGwire go by?

    a. Mick

    b. Big Mac

    c. Marky Mac

    d. Down to the McGwire

2. Eric Chavez goes by the nickname "Chavvy."

    a. True

    b. False

3. What nickname does Bert Campaneris go by?

    a. Bertie

    b. Camper

    c. Campy

    d. Batting Bert

4. What nickname does Reggie Jackson go by?

    a. Mr. April

    b. Mr. November

c. Mr. September

d. Mr. October

5. What nickname does Matt Chapman go by?

    a. Cougar

    b. Chappy

    c. Quick Cat

    d. Matty Chap

6. Which nickname does Sal Bando go by?

    a. Mr. Sal

    b. Captain Bando

    c. Captain Sal

    d. Mr. B

7. "Coco" is a nickname. Coco Crisp's full name is "Covelli Loyce Crisp.."

    a. True

    b. False

8. What nickname does Dennis Eckersley go by?

    a. Tall Guy

    b. Big Unit

    c. Den

    d. Eck

9. What nickname did Dave Henderson go by?

    a. Cobra

    b. Rattlesnake

    c. Hendu

    d. Hyena

10. "Blue Moon" is a nickname. What is Blue Moon Odom's full name?

    a. Johnny Lee Odom
    b. Lee Johnny Odom
    c. James Lamar Odom
    d. Lamar James Odom

11. "Catfish" is a nickname. What is Catfish Hunter's full name?

    a. Arthur Jacob Hunter
    b. Jacob Arthur Hunter
    c. Augustus James Hunter
    d. James Augustus Hunter

12. Rollie Fingers' full name is Roland Glen Fingers.

    a. True
    b. False

13. Which nickname does Kurt Suzuki go by?

    a. Lemur
    b. Aloha Kurt
    c. Zuk
    d. The Flyin' Hawaiian

14. What nickname does Dave Stewart go by?

    a. Stew
    b. Smoke
    c. Snake
    d. Both A and B

15. A's manager Bob Melvin goes by the nickname "BoMel."

    a. True

    b. False

16. What nickname does Nick Swisher go by?

    a. Silver Bullet

    b. Swish

    c. Buckets

    d. Slammin'

17. Don Baylor went by the nicknames "Groove" and "The Sneak Thief."

    a. True

    b. False

18. What nickname does Sean Manaea go by?

    a. Baby Koala

    b. Baby Elephant

    c. Baby Giraffe

    d. Baby Bird

19. What nickname does Ramón Laureano go by?

    a. Fire

    b. Speed

    c. Firework

    d. Laser

20. Bartolo Colon goes by the nickname "Big Sexy."

    a. True

    b. False

QUIZ ANSWERS

1. B – Big Mac

2. A- True

3. C – Campy

4. D – Mr. October

5. B – Chappy

6. C – Captain Sal

7. A – True

8. D – Eck

9. C – Hendu

10. A – Johnny Lee Odom

11. D – James Augustus Hunter

12. A – True

13. C – Zuk

14. D – Both A and B

15. A - True

16. B – Swish

17. A – True

18. C – Baby Giraffe

19. D – Laser

20. A – True

DID YOU KNOW?

1. Matt Olson goes by the nickname "Oly."

2. Josh Donaldson goes by the nickname "Bringer of Rain."

3. Gene Tenace goes by the nickname "Steamboat."

4. Tim Hudson goes by the nickname "Huddy."

5. Eric Byrnes goes by the nickname "Byrnesie."

6. Miguel Tejada goes by the nickname "Miggy."

7. Jason Giambi goes by the nickname "Giambino."

8. Frank Thomas goes by the nickname "the Big Hurt."

9. "Goose" is a nickname. Goose Gossage's full name is "Richard Michael Gossage."

10. Rickey Henderson goes by the nickname "Man of Steal."

CHAPTER 5:

ECK

QUIZ TIME!

1. What is Dennis Eckersley's full name?

    a. Dennis Louis Eckersley

    b. Louis Dennis Eckersley

    c. Lee Dennis Eckersley

    d. Dennis Lee Eckersley

2. Dennis Eckersley played his entire 24-season MLB career with the Oakland A's.

    a. True

    b. False

3. Where was Dennis Eckersley born?

    a. Walnut Creek, California

    b. Oakland, California

    c. San Diego, California

    d. Anaheim, California

4. When was Dennis Eckersley born?

a. May 3, 1958

b. May 31, 1958

c. October 3, 1954

d. October 31, 1954

5. Dennis Eckersley did NOT win a World Series championship during his 24- season MLB career.

a. True

b. False

6. How many MLB All-Star Games was Dennis Eckersley named to?

a. 2

b. 4

c. 6

d. 8

7. What year was Dennis Eckersley inducted into the National Baseball Hall of Fame?

a. 2001

b. 2002

c. 2003

d. 2004

8. Dennis Eckersley was named the 1998 ALCS MVP.

a. True

b. False

9. What year was Dennis Eckersley named the AL MVP?

a. 1989

b. 1992

c. 1993

d. 1995

10. How many Rolaids Relief Man of the Year Awards did Dennis Eckersley win?

    a. 1

    b. 2

    c. 3

    d. 4

11. How many Cy Young Awards did Dennis Eckersley win?

    a. 1

    b. 2

    c. 3

    d. 4

12. Dennis Eckersley was named *The Sporting News* American League Pitcher of the Year for 1992.

    a. True

    b. False

13. Dennis Eckersley threw a no-hitter on May 30, _____.

    a. 1975

    b. 1977

    c. 1989

    d. 1992

14. Dennis Eckersley was named to the Major League Baseball All-Time Team in 1997.

a. True

b. False

15. How many saves did Dennis Eckersley collect?

    a. 220

    b. 290

    c. 320

    d. 390

16. How many strikeouts did Dennis Eckersley collect?

    a. 1,401

    b. 1,801

    c. 2,401

    d. 2,801

17. Dennis Eckersley's career ERA is 3.50.

    a. True

    b. False

18. How many wins did Dennis Eckersley collect?

    a. 177

    b. 187

    c. 197

    d. 207

19. How many losses did Dennis Eckersley collect?

    a. 161

    b. 171

    c. 181

    d. 191

20. Dennis Eckersley pitched a total of 3,285.2 innings.

    a. True

    b. False

QUIZ ANSWERS

1. D – Dennis Lee Eckersley

2. B – False (He pitched for the Oakland A's, Boston Red Sox, Chicago Cubs, Cleveland Indians, and St. Louis Cardinals)

3. B – Oakland, California

4. C – October 3, 1954

5. B – False (1 in 1989)

6. C – 6

7. D – 2004

8. A – True

9. B – 1992

10. B – 2

11. A – 1 (1992)

12. A – True

13. B – 1977

14. A – True

15. D – 390

16. C – 2,401

17. A - True

18. C – 197

19. B – 171

20. A – True

DID YOU KNOW?

1. Dennis Eckersley's career WAR is 62.1.

2. Eckersley is a member of the Boston Red Sox Hall of Fame, as well as the Athletics Hall of Fame.

3. Eckersley is a 2x MLB saves leader (1988 and 1992).

4. Eckersley has been an analyst and commentator for Boston Red Sox broadcasts on NESN since 2003.

5. In 2017, Eckersley returned to the A's as a special assistant to team president, Dave Kaval.

6. When Tony La Russa left the A's to become the St. Louis Cardinals' manager, he was adamant that Eckersley come with him.

7. Growing up in the Bay Area, Eckersley was a fan of both the A's and the San Francisco Giants. His favorite players growing up were Willie Mays and Juan Marichal.

8. Eckersley played quarterback for his high school football team.

9. Eckersley's No. 43 was retired by the Oakland A's on August 13, 2005.

10. Eckersley is one of only two pitchers in MLB history to have both a 20-win season and 50-save season in their career.

CHAPTER 6:

STATISTICALLY SPEAKING

QUIZ TIME!

1. Mark McGwire holds the franchise record for career home runs with how many?

    a. 343
    b. 353
    c. 363
    d. 373

2. Pitcher Eddie Plank has the most wins in franchise history with 284.

    a. True
    b. False

3. Which pitcher holds the franchise record for career shutouts thrown with 59?

    a. Vida Blue
    b. Catfish Hunter
    c. Rube Waddell
    d. Eddie Plank

4. Which Oakland Athletics batter holds the single-season record for strikeouts with 197?

   a. Khris Davis

   b. Jack Cust

   c. Jose Canseco

   d. Reggie Jackson

5. Pitcher Eddie Plank has the most strikeouts in franchise history with .how many?

   a. 1,965

   b. 1,975

   c. 1,985

   d. 1.995

6. Rickey Henderson has the most stolen bases in Oakland Athletics franchise history with how many?

   a. 837

   b. 847

   c. 857

   d. 867

7. Dennis Eckersley holds the record for most saves in Oakland Athletics history with 320.

   a. True

   b. False

8. Who holds the Oakland Athletics record for being intentionally walked with 84.?

   a. Eric Chavez

   b. Sal Bando

c. Reggie Jackson

d. Mark McGwire

9. Who holds the Athletics franchise record for home runs in a single season with 58?

a. Mark McGwire

b. Jimmie Foxx

c. Khris Davis

d. Jose Canseco

10. Who holds the single-season franchise record for hits with 253?

a. Nap Lajoie

b. Doc Cramer

c. Miguel Tejada

d. Al Simmons

11. Who holds the single-season franchise record for double plays grounded into with 32?

a. Billy Butler

b. Ben Grieve

c. Jason Kendall

d. Billy Hitchcock

12. Mark McGwire holds the franchise record for sacrifice flies with 59.

a. True

b. False

13. Blue Moon Odom threw the most wild pitches in franchise history with .how many?

a. 67

b. 77

c. 87

d. 97

14. Home Run Baker holds the franchise's single-season record for most triples with how many in 1912?

a. 12

b. 15

c. 18

d. 21

15. Which hitter has the most walks in franchise history with 1,227?

a. Rickey Henderson

b. Max Bishop

c. Bob Johnson

d. Mark McGwire

16. Which Athletics hitter holds the all-time franchise record for best overall batting average at .356?

a. Eddie Collins

b. Nap Lajoie

c. Al Simmons

d. Jimmie Foxx

17. Bert Campaneris holds the franchise record for most runs scored with 1,270.

a. True

b. False

18. Bert Campaneris has the most plate appearances in franchise history with .how many?

    a. 6,327
    b. 6,994
    c. 7,481
    d. 7.895

19. Which pitcher holds the franchise record for most saves in a single season with 51?

    a. Grant Balfour
    b. Huston Street
    c. Dennis Eckersley
    d. Andrew Bailey

20. Eddie Plank holds the Athletics franchise record for most losses with 162.

    a. True
    b. False

QUIZ ANSWERS

1. C – 363

2. A - True

3. D – Eddie Plank

4. B – Jack Cust (2008)

5. C – 1,985

6. D – 867

7. A – True

8. C – Reggie Jackson

9. B – Jimmie Foxx (1932)

10. D – Al Simmons (1925)

11. B – Ben Grieve (2000)

12. A – True

13. C – 87

14. D – 21

15. A – Rickey Henderson

16. C – Al Simmons

17. B – False, Rickey Henderson

18. D – 7,895

19. C – Dennis Eckersley (1992)

20. A – True

DID YOU KNOW?

1. Eddie Plank threw the most innings in Athletics franchise history with 3,860.2. Coming in second is Charles Bender who threw 2,602 innings.

2. Nap Lajoie had the best single-season batting average in franchise history at .426 in 1901. Coming in second is Al Simmons whose batting average was .392 in 1927.

3. Stan Javier holds the franchise record for stolen base percentage with 85.83% success. Rickey Henderson holds the franchise record for career stolen bases with 867. Rickey Henderson also holds the franchise record for the most times caught stealing at 219.

4. Al Simmons has the most extra-base hits in franchise history with 655. Second on the list is Jimmie Foxx with 638.

5. Mark McGwire holds the Athletics franchise record for at-bats per home run at 12.3, meaning that, on average, Big Mac hit a home run about every 12 to 13 at-bats.

6. Dennis Eckersley holds the franchise record for strikeouts per 9 innings pitched at 9.297. This means is that Eck recorded about 9 to 10 strikeouts in every 9 innings that he pitched.

7. Jimmy Dykes holds the Athletics record for the most hit by pitches with 93. Eddie Plank holds the record for most batters hit with 179.

8. Jimmy Dykes holds the franchise record for career doubles hit with 365. Second on the list is Al Simmons with 348.

9. Jack Coombs and Lefty Grove are tied for the Athletics single-season record for wins with 31 each. Coombs won 31 in 1910 and Grove won 31 in 1931. Scott Perry holds the Oakland Athletics single-season record for most losses with 25 in 1920.

10. Rube Waddell holds the franchise record for most strikeouts by a pitcher in a single season with 349 in 1904.

CHAPTER 7:

THE TRADE MARKET

QUIZ TIME!

1. On November 29, 1971, the Oakland Athletics traded Rick Monday to which team for Ken Holtzman?

    a. Los Angeles Dodgers

    b. New York Yankees

    c. Chicago Cubs

    d. Baltimore Orioles

2. On April 3, 1987, the Oakland Athletics traded Brian Guinn, Mark Leonette, and Dave Wilder to the Chicago Cubs for what player and Dan Rohn?

    a. Curt Young

    b. Dave Stewart

    c. Rick Honeycutt

    d. Dennis Eckersley

3. The Oakland Athletics have made 12 trades with the Arizona Diamondbacks as of the end of the 2020 season.

    a. True

    b. False

4. On June 21, 1989, the Oakland Athletics traded Greg Cadaret, Eric Plunk, and Luis Polonia to the New York Yankees for what player?

    a. Bob Welch
    b. Dave Henderson
    c. Rickey Henderson
    d. Walt Weiss

5. The Oakland Athletics have made 16 trades with the Houston Astros (as of the end of 2020).

    a. True
    b. False

6. On December 18, 2004 the Oakland Athletics traded Mark Mulder to the for Dan Haren, Daric Barton and Kiko Calero.

    a. Arizona Diamondbacks
    b. St. Louis Cardinals
    c. Los Angeles Angels of Anaheim
    d. Los Angeles Dodgers

7. On December 14, 2007, the Oakland Athletics traded Dan Haren and Connor Robertson to what team for Brett Anderson, Dana Eveland, Greg Smith, Carlos Gonzalez, Aaron Cunningham, and Chris Carter?

    a. Colorado Rockies
    b. Milwaukee Brewers
    c. Arizona Diamondbacks
    d. Houston Astros

8. On July 8, 2008, the Oakland Athletics traded Rich Harden and Chad Gaudin to what team for Josh Donaldson, Sean Gallagher, Eric Patterson, and Matt Murton?

   a. Toronto Blue Jays
   b. Chicago Cubs
   c. Texas Rangers
   d. Minnesota Twins

9. On November 10, 2008, the Oakland Athletics traded Huston Street, Carlos Gonzalez, and Greg Smith to what team for Matt Holliday?

   a. San Diego Padres
   b. Los Angeles Angels of Anaheim
   c. St. Louis Cardinals
   d. Colorado Rockies

10. The Oakland Athletics have made only seven trades with the Florida/Miami Marlins (as of the end of the 2020 season).

    a. True
    b. False

11. On July 31, 2014, the Athletics traded Yoenis Cespedes to what team for Jon Lester and Jonny Gomes?

    a. Chicago Cubs
    b. Detroit Tigers
    c. Boston Red Sox
    d. New York Mets

12. The Oakland Athletics have made 11 trades with the Tampa Bay Rays (as of the end of the 2020 season).

    a. True

    b. False

13. On November 28, 2014, the Oakland Athletics traded Josh Donaldson to what team for Kendall Graveman, Sean Nolin, Brett Lawrie, and Franklin Barreto.

    a. Minnesota Twins

    b. Toronto Blue Jays

    c. Chicago White Sox

    d. Seattle Mariners

14. The Athletics have made 14 trades with the Colorado Rockies (as of the end of the 2020 season).

    a. True

    b. False

15. On August 31, 1992, the Athletics traded Jose Canseco to what team for Jeff Russell, Ruben Sierra, Bobby Witt, and cash considerations?

    a. Tampa Bay Devil Rays

    b. Boston Red Sox

    c. New York Yankees

    d. Texas Rangers

16. On July 31, 1997, the Oakland Athletics traded Mark McGwire to what team for Eric Ludwick, T.J. Mathews, and Blake Stein?

a. St. Louis Cardinals

b. Los Angeles Dodgers

c. San Diego Padres

d. Montreal Expos

17. On April 2, 1976, the Athletics traded Reggie Jackson, Ken Holtzman, and Bill VanBommel to what team for Don Baylor, Paul Mitchell, and Mike Torrez.

a. Boston Red Sox

b. Baltimore Orioles

c. California Angels

d. New York Yankees

18. On January 3, 2008, the Oakland Athletics traded Nick Swisher to what team for Gio Gonzalez, Ryan Sweeney, and Fautino De Los Santos?

a. New York Yankees

b. Cleveland Indians

c. Chicago White Sox

d. Atlanta Braves

19. On July 16, 2017, the Oakland Athletics traded Sean Doolittle and Ryan Madson to what team for Jesus Luzardo, Blake Treinen, and Sheldon Neuse.

a. Philadelphia Phillies

b. Washington Nationals

c. Cincinnati Reds

d. Kansas City Royals

20. The Oakland Athletics have made 15 trades with the Philadelphia Phillies (as of the end of the 2020 season).

    a. True
    b. False

QUIZ ANSWERS

1. C – Chicago Cubs

2. D – Dennis Eckersley

3. A – True

4. C – Rickey Henderson

5. A- True

6. B – St. Louis Cardinals

7. C – Arizona Diamondbacks

8. B – Chicago Cubs

9. D – Colorado Rockies

10. A- True

11. C – Boston Red Sox

12. A – True

13. B – Toronto Blue Jays

14. A – True

15. D – Texas Rangers

16. A – St. Louis Cardinals

17. B – Baltimore Orioles

18. C – Chicago White Sox

19. B – Washington Nationals

20. A- True

DID YOU KNOW?

1. On December 8, 1987, the Oakland Athletics traded Jose Rijo and Tim Birtsas to the Cincinnati Reds for Dave Parker.

2. On March 15, 1978, the Oakland Athletics traded Vida Blue to the San Francisco Giants for Gary Alexander, Dave Heaverlo, Phil Huffman, John Henry Johnson, Gary Thomasson, Alan Wirth, a PTBNL (Mario Guerrero), and $300,000.

3. On May 20, 1975, the Oakland Athletics traded Blue Moon Odom and cash considerations to the Cleveland Indians for Dick Bosman and Jim Perry.

4. On March 24, 1973, the Oakland Athletics traded Dave Duncan and George Hendrick to the Cleveland Indians for Ray Fosse and Jack Heidemann.

5. On August 3, 2012, the Oakland Athletics traded Kurt Suzuki and cash considerations to the Washington Nationals for David Freitas. On August 23, 2013, he was traded back to the A's by the Nationals for Dakota Bacus.

6. On June 30, 2011, the Oakland Athletics traded Mark Ellis to the Colorado Rockies for Bruce Billings and a PTBNL (Eliezer Mesa).

7. On August 31, 2016, the Oakland Athletics traded Coco Crisp and cash considerations to the Cleveland Indians for Colt Hynes.

8. On November 26, 2003, the Oakland Athletics traded Ramon Hernandez and Terrence Long to the San Diego Padres for Mark Kotsay.

9. On July 13, 2005, the Oakland Athletics traded Eric Byrnes and Omar Quintanilla to the Colorado Rockies for Joe Kennedy and Jay Witasick.

10. On August 1, 2016, the Oakland Athletics traded Josh Reddick and Rich Hill to the Los Angeles Dodgers for Frankie Montas, Jharel Cotton, and Grant Holmes.

CHAPTER 8:

DRAFT DAY

QUIZ TIME!

1. With the _____ overall pick in the 1st round of the 2014 MLB draft, the Oakland Athletics selected Matt Chapman.

    a. 10th
    b. 15th
    c. 20th
    d. 25th

2. With the _____ overall pick in the 1st round of the 2012 MLB draft, the Oakland Athletics selected Matt Olson.

    a. 27th
    b. 37th
    c. 47th
    d. 57th

3. With the _____ overall pick in the 1st round of the 1984 MLB draft, the Oakland Athletics selected Mark McGwire.

    a. 3rd
    b. 10th

   c. 13th

   d. 20th

4. Rickey Henderson was drafted by the Oakland Athletics in the _____ round of the 1976 MLB draft.

   a. 2nd

   b. 3rd

   c. 4th

   d. 5th

5. With the _____ overall pick in the 1st round of the 1996 MLB draft, the Oakland Athletics selected Eric Chavez.

   a. 2nd

   b. 3rd

   c. 10th

   d. 11th

6. Kurt Suzuki was drafted by the Oakland Athletics in the 2nd round of the _____ MLB draft.

   a. 2002

   b. 2004

   c. 2006

   d. 2007

7. Dave Stewart was drafted by the Los Angeles Dodgers in the 16th round of the 1975 MLB draft.

   a. True

   b. False

8. Jason Giambi was drafted by the Oakland Athletics in the _____ round of the 1992 MLB draft.

a. 2nd

b. 4th

c. 6th

d. 8th

9. Jose Canseco was drafted by the Oakland Athletics in the _____ round of the 1982 MLB draft.

a. 2nd

b. 5th

c. 10th

d. 15th

10. Huston Street was drafted by the Athletics in the 1st round (40th overall) of the 2004 MLB draft.

a. True

b. False

11. With the _____ overall pick in the 1st round of the 2002 MLB draft, the Oakland Athletics selected Nick Swisher.

a. 8th

b. 16th

c. 20th

d. 24th

12. Reggie Jackson was drafted by the Kansas City Athletics in the 1st round (2nd overall) of the 1966 MLB draft.

a. True

b. False

13. Sal Bando was drafted by the Kansas City Athletics in the _____ round of the 1965 MLB draft.

a. 2nd

b. 4th

c. 6th

d. 8th

14. With the _____ overall pick in the 1st round of the 1985 MLB draft, the Oakland Athletics selected Walt Weiss.

a. 4th

b. 7th

c. 11th

d. 17th

15. Dennis Eckersley was drafted by what team in the 3rd round of the 1972 MLB draft?

a. Boston Red Sox

b. Cleveland Indians

c. Chicago Cubs

d. St. Louis Cardinals

16. With the 7th overall pick in the 1st round of the 1989 MLB draft, what team selected Frank Thomas?

a. Chicago Cubs

b. Atlanta Braves

c. Toronto Blue Jays

d. Chicago White Sox

17. Rick Honeycutt was drafted by what team in the 17th round of the 1976 MLB draft?

a. Seattle Mariners

b. Texas Rangers

c. Los Angeles Dodgers

d. Pittsburgh Pirates

18. With the 26th overall pick in the 1st round of the 1977 MLB draft, what team selected Dave Henderson?

    a. San Francisco Giants

    b. Kansas City Royals

    c. Boston Red Sox

    d. Seattle Mariners

19. Terry Steinbach was drafted by the Oakland Athletics in what round of the 1983 MLB draft?

    a. 3rd

    b. 9th

    c. 12th

    d. 15th

20. Carney Lansford was drafted by the California Angels in the 3rd round of the 1975 MLB draft.

    a. True

    b. False

QUIZ ANSWERS

1. D – 25th

2. C – 47th

3. B – 10th

4. C – 4th

5. C – 10th

6. B – 2004

7. A – True

8. A – 2nd

9. D – 15th

10. A – True

11. B – 16th

12. A – True

13. C – 6th

14. C – 11th

15. B – Cleveland Indians

16. D – Chicago White Sox

17. D – Pittsburgh Pirates

18. D – Seattle Mariners

19. B – 9th

20. A – True

DID YOU KNOW?

1. Eric Byrnes was drafted in the 8th round of the 1998 MLB draft by the Oakland Athletics.

2. Jed Lowrie was drafted in the 1st round (45th overall) in the 2005 MLB draft by the Boston Red Sox.

3. Mark Ellis was drafted in the 9th round of the 1999 MLB draft by the Kansas City Royals.

4. Bobby Crosby was drafted in the 1st round (25th overall) of the 2001 MLB draft by the Oakland Athletics.

5. Jed Lowrie was drafted in the 1st round (45th overall) of the 2005 MLB draft by the Boston Red Sox.

6. Coco Crisp was drafted in the 7th round of the 1999 MLB draft by the St. Louis Cardinals.

7. Tim Hudson was drafted in the 6th round of the 1997 MLB draft by the Oakland Athletics.

8. Barry Zito was drafted in the 1st round (9th overall) of the 1999 MLB draft by the Oakland Athletics.

9. Ray Fosse was drafted in the 1st round (7th overall) of the 1965 MLB draft by the Cleveland Indians.

10. Current A's manager, Bob Melvin was drafted in the 1st round (2nd overall) of the 1981 MLB draft by the Detroit Tigers.

CHAPTER 9:

ODDS & ENDS

QUIZ TIME!

1. Former Athletic Nick Swisher is married to which Hollywood actress?

    a. Hilary Duff

    b. Joanna Garcia

    c. Lea Michele

    d. Anna Kendrick

2. Jason Giambi's brother, Jeremy, also played for the Oakland A's.

    a. True

    b. False

3. Former Athletic Yonder Alonso's brother-in-law (wife's brother) also plays in the MLB. Who is he?

    a. Bryce Harper

    b. Kris Bryant

    c. Manny Machado

    d. Clayton Kershaw

4. In 2019, Eric Byrnes set the Guinness World Record for what event?

    a. Fastest 100-meter hurdles wearing swim fins
    b. Most holes of golf in a single day
    c. Most pull-ups in 24 hours
    d. Fastest 50 meters walking on hands with a soccer ball between the legs

5. In a high school football game, former Athletic Johnny Damon suffered his first sports injury at the hands of which NFL star?

    a. Ronnie Lott
    b. Michael Strahan
    c. Troy Polamalu
    d. Warren Sapp

6. When Stephen Vogt was with the Oakland A's, he did an impersonation of which popular *Saturday Night Live* (SNL) sketch character?

    a. MacGruber
    b. Matt Foley ("Van Down by the River" guy)
    c. Stefon
    d. Church Lady

7. Former A's manager Tony La Russa has a no-kill pet shelter in Walnut Creek, California, called "Tony La Russa's Animal Rescue Foundation" (ARF).

    a. True
    b. False

8. Jose Canseco's twin brother, Ozzie also played Major League Baseball.

   a. True
   b. False

9. Which country singer did Elvis Andrus listen to when he was a teenager to help him learn English?

   a. Carrie Underwood
   b. Shania Twain
   c. Rascal Flatts
   d. Tim McGraw

10. Frank Thomas owns his own beer brand, called
    _____.

    a. Thomas Beer & Co.
    b. Big Hurt Brew
    c. Frank's Brew
    d. Big Hurt Beer

11. Who has played for more MLB teams than any other player in MLB history?

    a. Rajai Davis
    b. Rickey Henderson
    c. Edwin Jackson
    d. Bartolo Colon

12. Former Athletic Jim Perry is the brother of Hall of Fame pitcher Gaylord Perry.

    a. True
    b. False

13. Dave Parker owned several _____ franchises in Cincinnati for 25 years.

    a. McDonald's
    b. Popeye's Chicken
    c. Starbucks
    d. Dunkin Donuts

14. Milton Bradley's great-great-grandfather created the game company Milton Bradley.

    a. True
    b. False

15. Which BRAVO reality show has Johnny Damon appeared on twice?

    a. *Vanderpump Rules*
    b. *The Real Housewives of Beverly Hills*
    c. *Below Deck*
    d. *Southern Charm*

16. Jason Kendall authored a book entitled: *Throwback: A Big-League Catcher Tells How the Game Is Really Played,* released in May of 2014.

    a. True
    b. False

17. David DeJesus' wife, Kim was a contestant on which reality show?

    a. *Big Brother*
    b. *Survivor*

c. *The Amazing Race*

d. *American Idol*

18. Bert Campaneris is a cousin of which former MLB player?

    a. Leo Cardenas

    b. Jose Cardenal

    c. Paul Casanova

    d. Mike Cuellar

19. Rick Honeycutt was the pitching coach for what team from 2006 to 2019?

    a. St. Louis Cardinals

    b. Oakland A's

    c. Texas Rangers

    d. Los Angeles Dodgers

20. Rickey Henderson is known for referring to himself in the third person.

    a. True

    b. False

QUIZ ANSWERS

1. B – Joanna Garcia

2. A – True

3. C – Manny Machado

4. B – Most holes of golf in a single day (420 holes)

5. D – Warren Sapp

6. B – Matt Foley ("Van Down by the River" guy)

7. A – True

8. A – True

9. C – Rascal Flatts

10. D – Big Hurt Beer

11. C – Edwin Jackson

12. A – True

13. B – Popeye's Chicken

14. B – False

15. C – *Below Deck*

16. A – True

17. C – *The Amazing Race*

18. B – Jose Cardenal

19. D – Los Angeles Dodgers

20. A – True

DID YOU KNOW?

1. The Oscar-nominated film *Moneyball* is based on the Oakland A's of the early 2000s. Billy Beane is played by Brad Pitt, Scott Hatteberg is played by Chris Pratt, Art Howe was played by Philip Seymour Hoffman, and David Justice was played by Stephen Bishop.

2. In July 2017, Coco Crisp became the head coach of the Shadow Hills High School baseball team. In 2019, he joined the Oakland Athletics Radio Network as a color analyst part-time.

3. When Bartolo Colon was 42 years old, he became the oldest MLB player to hit his first career home run. At 45 years old, he was the oldest active MLB player and the last active MLB player who had played for the Montreal Expos. He also holds the record for most wins by a Latin-American-born pitcher.

4. In 2011, Nick Swisher released a children's album called "Believe," which featured fellow MLB players Barry Zito and Bernie Williams. It peaked at No. 3 on iTunes' Top Children's Albums.

5. Josh Reddick is an avid wrestling fan. He even wrote an article about his love for wrestling in *The Player's Tribune.*

6. Dusty Baker was a member of the United States Marine Corps Reserve from 1969-1975.

7. Joe Blanton and his wife own a 3-acre vineyard on Howell Mountain that produces cabernet sauvignon in St. Helena, California.

8. On February 4, 2015, Matt Stairs was elected to the Canadian Baseball Hall of Fame.

9. From 1997 to 2006, Dave Henderson worked as a color commentator during Seattle Mariners radio and television broadcasts.

10. John Axford has a bachelor's degree in film and television from Notre Dame University.

CHAPTER 10:

OUTFIELDERS

QUIZ TIME!

1. What year was Reggie Jackson inducted into the National Baseball Hall of Fame?

   a. 1990

   b. 1993

   c. 1995

   d. 1999

2. Dwayne Murphy won six Gold Glove Awards during his 12-season MLB career.

   a. True

   b. False

3. How many World Series championships did Joe Rudi win in his 16-season MLB career?

   a. 0

   b. 1

   c. 2

   d. 3

4. Jose Canseco's career batting average is .266.

   a. True
   b. False

5. What year was Rickey Henderson named the American League MVP?

   a. 1981
   b. 1985
   c. 1990
   d. 1995

6. How many seasons did Coco Crisp spend with the Oakland A's?

   a. 5
   b. 6
   c. 7
   d. 9

7. During his 19-season MLB career, Rick Monday was named to two MLB All-Star Games.

   a. True
   b. False

8. In his 14-season MLB career, Jermaine Dye played for the Oakland A's, Kansas City Royals, Atlanta Braves, and what other team?

   a. New York Yankees
   b. Chicago White Sox
   c. Texas Rangers
   d. Colorado Rockies

9. How many MLB All-Star Games was Johnny Damon named to during his 18-season MLB career?

    a. 1
    b. 2
    c. 5
    d. 6

10. How many seasons did Dave Henderson spend with the Oakland A's?

    a. 2
    b. 4
    c. 6
    d. 8

11. In his 17-season MLB career, Mark Kotsay played for the Oakland A's, Florida Marlins, Chicago White Sox, Boston Red Sox, Atlanta Braves, Milwaukee Brewers, and what other team?

    a. Los Angeles Dodgers
    b. Washington Nationals
    c. San Diego Padres
    d. Colorado Rockies

12. Nick Swisher was named to four MLB All-Star Games during his 12-season MLB career.

    a. True
    b. False

13. How many seasons did Eric Byrnes spend with the Oakland A's?

a. 2

b. 4

c. 6

d. 8

14. Ben Grieve was named the _____ American League Rookie of the Year.

    a. 1997

    b. 1998

    c. 1999

    d. 2000

15. How many Silver Slugger Awards did Don Baylor win during his 19-season MLB career?

    a. 1

    b. 2

    c. 3

    d. 4

16. How many seasons did Stan Javier spend with the Oakland A's?

    a. 3

    b. 5

    c. 7

    d. 9

17. Yoenis Cespedes won back-to-back Home Run Derbies in what years?

    a. 2012 and 2013

    b. 2013 and 2014

c. 2014 and 2015

d. 2015 and 2016

18. Josh Reddick won a Gold Glove Award while with the Oakland A's in what year?

    a. 2012

    b. 2013

    c. 2014

    d. 2015

19. How many seasons did Whitey Herzog spend with the Kansas City Athletics?

    a. 1

    b. 2

    c. 3

    d. 4

20. Dusty Baker spent two seasons of his 19-season MLB career with the Oakland A's.

    a. True

    b. False

QUIZ ANSWERS

1. B – 1993

2. A – True

3. D – 3

4. A – True

5. C – 1990

6. C – 7

7. A – True

8. B – Chicago White Sox

9. B – 2

10. C – 6

11. C – San Diego Padres

12. B – False, 1

13. C – 6

14. B – 1998

15. C – 3

16. C – 7

17. B – 2013 and 2014

18. A – 2012

19. C – 3

20. A – True

DID YOU KNOW?

1. Rickey Henderson spent 14 seasons of his MLB career with the Oakland Athletics. He also played for the New York Yankees, San Diego Padres, New York Mets, Boston Red Sox, Los Angeles Angels, Anaheim Angels, Seattle Mariners, and Toronto Blue Jays. He is a member of the National Baseball Hall of Fame, MVP, 10x MLB All-Star, 2x World Series champion, Gold Glove Award winner, 3x Silver Slugger Award winner, and ALCS MVP.

2. Reggie Jackson spent 10 seasons of his MLB career with the Oakland Athletics. He also played for the New York Yankees, California Angels, and Baltimore Orioles. He is a member of the National Baseball Hall of Fame, MVP, 14x MLB All-Star, 5x World Series champion, 2x Silver Slugger Award, 2x World Series MVP, and Major League Player of the Year.

3. Jose Canseco spent nine seasons of his MLB career with the Oakland Athletics. He also played for the Texas Rangers, Tampa Bay Devil Rays, Boston Red Sox, New York Yankees, Chicago White Sox, and Toronto Blue Jays. He is a 6x MLB All-Star, 4x Silver Slugger Award winner, MVP, American League Rookie of the Year, and 2x World Series champion.

4. Joe Rudi spent 11 seasons of his MLB career with the Oakland Athletics. He also played for the California

81

Angels and Boston Red Sox. He is a 3x MLB All-Star, 3x World Series champion, and 3x Gold Glove Award winner.

5. Jermaine Dye spent four seasons of his MLB career with the Oakland Athletics. He also played for the Kansas City Royals, Chicago White Sox, and Atlanta Braves. He is a 2x MLB All-Star, Silver Slugger Award winner, Gold Glove Award winner, World Series champion, and World Series MVP.

6. Dave Henderson spent six seasons of his MLB career with the Oakland Athletics. He also played for the Seattle Mariners, Boston Red Sox, Kansas City Royals, and San Francisco Giants. He was an MLB All-Star and 1989 World Series champion.

7. Nick Swisher spent four seasons of his MLB career with the Oakland Athletics. He also played for the New York Yankees, Chicago White Sox, Cleveland Indians, and Atlanta Braves. He is an MLB All-Star and World Series champion.

8. Don Baylor spent two seasons of his MLB career with the Oakland Athletics. He also played for the California Angels, Baltimore Orioles, New York Yankees, Boston Red Sox, and Minnesota Twins. He was an MVP, MLB All-Star, World Series champion, 3x Silver Slugger Award winner, and Manager of the Year Award winner.

9. Dusty Baker spent two seasons of his MLB career with the Oakland Athletics. He also played for the Los Angeles

Dodgers, Atlanta Braves, and San Francisco Giants. He is a 2x MLB All-Star, World Series champion, Gold Glove Award winner, 2x Silver Slugger Award winner, NLCS MVP, and 3x Manager of the Year Award winner.

10. Yoenis Cespedes spent three seasons of his MLB career with the Oakland Athletics. He also played for the New York Mets, Detroit Tigers, and Boston Red Sox. He is a 2x MLB All-Star, Silver Slugger Award winner, and Gold Glove Award winner.

CHAPTER 11:

INFIELDERS

QUIZ TIME!

1. How many Gold Glove Awards did Eric Chavez win during his 17-season MLB career?

   a. 2
   b. 4
   c. 6
   d. 8

2. Mark McGwire's career batting average is .263.

   a. True
   b. False

3. As of the end of the 2020 season, how many Platinum Glove Awards has Matt Chapman won?

   a. 1
   b. 2
   c. 3
   d. 4

4. How many MLB All-Star Games was Sal Bando named to in his 16-season MLB career?

    a. 1

    b. 2

    c. 3

    d. 4

5. How many MLB All-Star Games was Bert Campaneris named to in his 19-season MLB career?

    a. 2

    b. 4

    c. 6

    d. 8

6. Walt Weiss was named the _____ American League Rookie of the Year.

    a. 1987

    b. 1988

    c. 1989

    d. 1990

7. As of the end of the 2020 season, Matt Olson has won two Gold Glove Awards.

    a. True

    b. False

8. How many seasons did Carney Lansford spend with the Oakland A's?

    a. 4

    b. 6

c. 8

d. 10

9. How many seasons did Mark Ellis spend with the Oakland A's?

    a. 6

    b. 7

    c. 9

    d. 11

10. During his 20-season MLB career, Jason Giambi played for the Oakland A's, Colorado Rockies, Cleveland Indians, and what other team?

    a. Texas Rangers

    b. New York Yankees

    c. New York Mets

    d. Boston Red Sox

11. Bobby Crosby was named the _____ American League Rookie of the Year.

    a. 2003

    b. 2004

    c. 2005

    d. 2006

12. Dick Green spent his entire 12-season MLB career with the Kansas City/Oakland A's.

    a. True

    b. False

13. How many MLB All-Star Games was Marco Scutaro named to in his 13-season MLB career?

    a. 1
    b. 2
    c. 3
    d. 4

14. Jed Lowrie was named to the MLB All-Star Game in what year?

    a. 2013
    b. 2014
    c. 2016
    d. 2018

15. As of the end of the 2020 season, how many Silver Slugger Awards has Josh Donaldson won?

    a. 0
    b. 1
    c. 2
    d. 3

16. Miguel Tejada was named the 2002 American League MVP.

    a. True
    b. False

17. What year was Joe Morgan inducted into the National Baseball Hall of Fame?

    a. 1987
    b. 1989

c. 1990

d. 1993

18. What year was Frank Thomas inducted into the National Baseball Hall of Fame?

a. 2012

b. 2014

c. 2016

d. 2018

19. Wayne Gross spent nine seasons with the Oakland A's and one season with what club?

a. New York Mets

b. St. Louis Cardinals

c. Boston Red Sox

d. Baltimore Orioles

20. Marcus Semien spent six seasons with the Oakland A's.

a. True

b. False

QUIZ ANSWERS

1. C – 6

2. A- True

3. B – 2

4. D – 4

5. C – 6

6. B – 1988

7. A – True

8. D – 10

9. C – 9

10. B – New York Yankees

11. B – 2004

12. A – True

13. A – 1

14. D – 2018

15. C – 2

16. A – True

17. C – 1990

18. B – 2014

19. D – Baltimore Orioles

20. A – True

DID YOU KNOW?

1. Eric Chavez spent 13 seasons of his MLB career with the Oakland Athletics. He also played for the New York Yankees and Arizona Diamondbacks. He is a 6x Gold Glove Award winner and Silver Slugger Award winner.

2. Mark McGwire spent 12 seasons of his MLB career with the Oakland Athletics. He also played for the St. Louis Cardinals. He is a 12x MLB All-Star, AL Rookie of the Year, 1989 World Series champion, Gold Glove Award winner, and 3x Silver Slugger Award winner.

3. Matt Chapman and Matt Olson both currently play for the Oakland Athletics. Chapman has been with the team since 2017 and Olson since 2016. As of the end of the 2020 season, Chapman is an MLB All-Star, 2x Gold Glove Award winner, 2x Platinum Glove Award winner, and Wilson Overall Defensive Player of the Year. As of the end of the 2020 season, Olson is a 2x Gold Glove Award winner.

4. Sal Bando spent 11 seasons of his MLB career with the Oakland Athletics. He also played for the Milwaukee Brewers. He is a 4x MLB All-Star and 3x World Series champion.

5. Bert Campaneris spent 13 seasons of his MLB career with the Oakland Athletics. He also played for the Texas

Rangers, California Angels, and New York Yankees. He is a 6x MLB All-Star and 3x World Series champion.

6. Walt Weiss spent 6 seasons of his MLB career with the Oakland Athletics He also played for the Colorado Rockies, Atlanta Braves, and Florida Marlins. He is an MLB All-Star, AL Rookie of the Year, and 1989 World Series champion. He was the Colorado Rockies' manager from 2013 to 2016.

7. Carney Lansford spent 10 seasons of his MLB career with the Oakland Athletics. He also played for the California Angels, and Boston Red Sox. He is a 1x MLB All-Star, 1989 World Series champion, Silver Slugger Award winner, and batting title winner.

8. Miguel Tejada spent seven seasons of his MLB career with the Oakland Athletics. He also played for the Baltimore Orioles, Houston Astros, Kansas City Royals, San Diego Padres, and San Francisco Giants. He is an MVP, 6x MLB All-Star, 2x Silver Slugger Award winner, and All-Star Game MVP.

9. Jason Giambi spent eight seasons of his MLB career with the Oakland Athletics. He also played for the Colorado Rockies, New York Yankees, and Cleveland Indians. He is an MVP, 5x MLB All-Star, and 2x Silver Slugger Award winner.

10. Frank Thomas spent two seasons of his MLB career with the Oakland Athletics. He also played for the Chicago White Sox and Toronto Blue Jays. He is a member of the

National Baseball Hall of Fame, 2x MVP, 5x MLB All-Star, 4x Silver Slugger Award winner, batting title champion, and Major League Player of the Year.

CHAPTER 12:

PITCHERS AND CATCHERS

QUIZ TIME!

1. What year was Catfish Hunter inducted into the National Baseball Hall of Fame?

   a. 1985

   b. 1986

   c. 1987

   d. 1988

2. Dave Stewart spent his entire 16-season MLB career with the Oakland Athletics.

   a. True

   b. False

3. How many Gold Glove Awards did Ray Fosse win in his 12-season MLB career?

   a. 1

   b. 2

   c. 3

   d. 4

4. How many MLB All-Star Games was Terry Steinbach named to during his 14-season MLB career?

    a. 1

    b. 2

    c. 3

    d. 4

5. How many seasons did Dennis Eckersley spend with the Oakland Athletics?

    a. 6

    b. 7

    c. 8

    d. 9

6. How many seasons did Rollie Fingers spend with the Oakland Athletics?

    a. 6

    b. 7

    c. 8

    d. 9

7. Huston Street was named the 2005 American League Rookie of the Year.

    a. True

    b. False

8. Vida Blue won both a Cy Young Award and the American League MVP Award with the A's in what year?

    a. 1969

    b. 1970

c.   1971

d.   1972

9.   Which pitcher was NOT a member of the Oakland Athletics' "Big Three"?

a.   Barry Zito

b.   Cory Lidle

c.   Mark Mulder

d.   Tim Hudson

10. How many seasons did Kurt Suzuki spend with the Oakland Athletics?

a.   5

b.   7

c.   8

d.   9

11. How many MLB All-Star Games was Jason Kendall named to in his 15-season MLB career?

a.   1

b.   2

c.   3

d.   4

12. Bob Welch won a Cy Young Award with the A's in 1990.

a.   True

b.   False

13. On which holiday did Dallas Braden throw his perfect game?

a. Memorial Day

b. 4th of July

c. Father's Day

d. Mother's Day

14. How many ERA Titles did Lefty Grove win during his 17-season MLB career?

a. 9

b. 8

c. 7

d. 6

15. How many seasons did Blue Moon Odom spend with the Oakland Athletics?

a. 9

b. 10

c. 11

d. 12

16. Ken Holtzman was named to two MLB All-Star Games in his 15-season MLB career.

a. True

b. False

17. How many different MLB teams did Bartolo Colon play for during his 21-season MLB career?

a. 9

b. 10

c. 11

d. 12

18. How many seasons did Rick Honeycutt spend with the Oakland Athletics?

    a. 6
    b. 8
    c. 9
    d. 10

19. How many seasons did Eddie Plank spend with the Philadelphia Athletics?

    a. 11
    b. 12
    c. 13
    d. 14

20. Sean Manaea threw a no-hitter with the A's in 2018.

    a. True
    b. False

QUIZ ANSWERS

1. C – 1987

2. B – False (A's, Los Angeles Dodgers, Texas Rangers, Philadelphia Phillies, and Toronto Blue Jays)

3. B – 2

4. C – 3

5. D – 9

6. D – 9

7. A – True

8. C – 1971

9. B – Cory Lidle

10. B – 7

11. C – 3

12. A – True

13. D – Mother's Day

14. A – 9

15. D – 12

16. A – True

17. C – 11

18. B – 8

19. D – 14

20. A – True

DID YOU KNOW?

1. Jim "Catfish" Hunter spent 10 seasons of his MLB career with the Oakland Athletics. He also played for the New York Yankees. He is a member of the National Baseball Hall of Fame, Cy Young Award winner, 8x MLB All-Star, 5x World Series champion, and ERA title winner.

2. Dave Stewart spent 8 seasons of his MLB career with the Oakland Athletics. He also played for the Los Angeles Dodgers, Texas Rangers, Philadelphia Phillies, and Toronto Blue Jays. He is a 1x MLB All-Star, 3x World Series champion, World Series MVP, and 2x ALCS MVP.

3. Dennis Eckersley spent nine seasons of his MLB career with the Oakland Athletics. He also played for the Boston Red Sox, Chicago Cubs, Cleveland Indians, and St. Louis Cardinals. He is a member of the National Baseball Hall of Fame, MVP, Cy Young Award winner, 6x MLB All-Star, 1989 World Series champion, ALCS MVP, and 2x Rolaids Relief Man of the Year.

4. Rollie Fingers spent nine seasons of his MLB career with the Oakland Athletics. He also played for the San Diego Padres and Milwaukee Brewers. He is a member of the National Baseball Hall of Fame, MVP, Cy Young Award winner, 7x MLB All-Star, 3x World Series champion, World Series MVP, and 4x Rolaids Relief Man of the Year.

5. Ray Fosse spent three seasons of his MLB career with the Oakland Athletics. He also played for the Cleveland Indians, Seattle Mariners, and Milwaukee Brewers. He is a 2x MLB All-Star, 2x Gold Glove Award winner, and 2x World Series champion. He is currently a commentator on A's TV and radio broadcasts.

6. Terry Steinbach spent 11 seasons of his MLB career with the Oakland Athletics. He also played for the Minnesota Twins. He is a 3x MLB All-Star, All-Star MVP, and 1989 World Series champion.

7. Vida Blue spent nine seasons of his MLB career with the Oakland Athletics. He also played for the Kansas City Royals and San Francisco Giants. He is an MVP, Cy Young Award winner, 6x MLB All-Star, 3x World Series champion, and ERA title winner.

8. Blue Moon Odom spent 12 seasons of his MLB career with the Oakland Athletics. He also played for the Atlanta Braves, Cleveland Indians, and Chicago White Sox. He is a 2x MLB All-Star and 3x World Series champion.

9. Bob Welch spent seven seasons of his MLB career with the Oakland Athletics. He also played for the Los Angeles Dodgers. He was a Cy Young Award winner, 2x MLB All-Star, and 2x World Series champion.

10. Rick Honeycutt spent eight seasons of his MLB career with the Oakland Athletics. He also played for the Los Angeles Dodgers, Texas Rangers, Seattle Mariners, St. Louis Cardinals, and New York Yankees. He is a 2x MLB All-Star, ERA title winner, and 1989 World Series champion.

CHAPTER 13:

WORLD SERIES

QUIZ TIME!

1. How many World Series championships have the Oakland Athletics won?

    a. 4

    b. 8

    c. 9

    d. 12

2. How many AL pennants have the Oakland Athletics won (as of the end of the 2020 season)?

    a. 5

    b. 8

    c. 10

    d. 15

3. How many wild card berths have the Oakland Athletics won (as of the end of the 2020 season)?

    a. 2

    b. 4

c. 6

d. 8

4. Which team did the Philadelphia Athletics face in the 1910 World Series?

    a. Philadelphia Phillies

    b. Pittsburgh Pirates

    c. Chicago Cubs

    d. New York Giants

5. How many games did the 1910 World Series go?

    a. 4

    b. 5

    c. 6

    d. 7

6. Which team did the Philadelphia Athletics face in the 1911 World Series?

    a. Philadelphia Phillies

    b. Pittsburgh Pirates

    c. Chicago Cubs

    d. New York Giants

7. The 1911 World Series went six games.

    a. True

    b. False

8. Which team did the Philadelphia Athletics face in the 1913 World Series?

    a. Philadelphia Phillies

    b. Pittsburgh Pirates

c. Chicago Cubs

d. New York Giants

9. How many games did the 1913 World Series go?

   a. 4

   b. 5

   c. 6

   d. 7

10. Which team did the Philadelphia Athletics face in the 1929 World Series?

   a. St. Louis Cardinals

   b. Pittsburgh Pirates

   c. Chicago Cubs

   d. New York Giants

11. How many games did the 1929 World Series go?

   a. 4

   b. 5

   c. 6

   d. 7

12. The Philadelphia Athletics faced the St. Louis Cardinals in the 1930 World Series.

   a. True

   b. False

13. How many games did the 1930 World Series go?

   a. 4

   b. 5

c. 6

d. 7

14. Which team did the Oakland Athletics face in the 1972 World Series?

    a. Chicago Cubs

    b. Houston Astros

    c. Pittsburgh Pirates

    d. Cincinnati Reds

15. How many games did the 1972 World Series go?

    a. 4

    b. 5

    c. 6

    d. 7

16. The Oakland Athletics faced the New York Mets in the 1973 World Series.

    a. True

    b. False

17. How many games did the 1973 World Series go?

    a. 4

    b. 5

    c. 6

    d. 7

18. Which team did the Oakland Athletics face in the 1974 World Series?

    a. Pittsburgh Pirates

    b. Los Angeles Dodgers

c. St. Louis Cardinals

d. Cincinnati Reds

19. How many games did the 1974 World Series go?

    a. 4

    b. 5

    c. 6

    d. 7

20. The Oakland Athletics swept the San Francisco Giants in the 1989 World Series.

    a. True

    b. False

QUIZ ANSWERS

1. C – 9

2. D – 15

3. B – 4

4. C – Chicago Cubs

5. B – 5

6. D – New York Giants

7. A – True

8. D – New York Giants

9. B – 5

10. C – Chicago Cubs

11. B – 5

12. A - True

13. C – 6

14. D – Cincinnati Reds

15. D – 7

16. A – True

17. D – 7

18. B – Los Angeles Dodgers

19. B – 5

20. A – True

DID YOU KNOW?

1. On October 17, 1989, the Loma Prieta earthquake shook the Bay Area just minutes before the first pitch of Game 3 in a World Series between the two Bay Area teams, the A's and Giants. Game 3 was finally played on October 27 after a 10-day delay.

2. Gene Tenace was named the 1972 World Series MVP.

3. Reggie Jackson was named the 1973 World Series MVP.

4. Rollie Fingers was named the 1974 World Series MVP.

5. Dave Stewart was named the 1989 World Series MVP.

6. Connie Mack was manager of the Philadelphia Athletics during the 1910, 1911, 1913, 1929, and 1930 World Series.

7. Dick Williams was manager of the Oakland Athletics during the 1972 and 1973 World Series.

8. Alvin Dark was manager of the Oakland Athletics during the 1974 World Series.

9. Tony La Russa was manager of the Oakland Athletics during the 1989 World Series.

10. The 1989 World Series was the last major sports championship for the city of Oakland until the Golden State Warriors won the NBA Finals in 2015.

CHAPTER 14:

HEATED RIVALRIES

QUIZ TIME!

1. Which team does NOT play in the American League West with the Oakland Athletics?

    a. Los Angeles Angels

    b. Kansas City Royals

    c. Seattle Mariners

    d. Texas Rangers

2. The Chicago White Sox, Minnesota Twins, and Kansas City Royals were all part of the American League West Division from 1969-1993.

    a. True

    b. False

3. Which team below was a member of the AL West Division from 1969 to 1971?

    a. San Francisco Giants

    b. Milwaukee Brewers

    c. San Diego Padres

    d. Los Angeles Dodgers

4. What current American League West team has the most AL West championships?

   a. Seattle Mariners
   b. Oakland A's
   c. Texas Rangers
   d. Los Angeles Angels

5. The Houston Astros moved to the AL West from the NL Central in 2013.

   a. True
   b. False

6. Which team won the American League West in 2020?

   a. Seattle Mariners
   b. Houston Astros
   c. Los Angeles Angels
   d. Oakland A's

7. The Milwaukee Brewers did NOT win an AL West championship during their time in the division.

   a. True
   b. False

8. The Athletics have won nine World Series championships. How many do the Seattle Mariners have?

   a. 0
   b. 1
   c. 2
   d. 3

9. The Athletics have won nine World Series championships. How many do the Los Angeles Angels have?

   a. 0

   b. 1

   c. 2

   d. 3

10. The Athletics have won nine World Series championships. How many do the Texas Rangers have?

   a. 0

   b. 1

   c. 2

   d. 3

11. The Athletics have won nine World Series championships. How many do the Houston Astros have?

   a. 0

   b. 1

   c. 2

   d. 3

12. The A's and Giants shared Candlestick Park for a short time, which is a big reason for their rivalry.

   a. True

   b. False

13. When the Oakland A's play their rival from across the Bay, the SF Giants, the series is called what?

   a. Bay Area Series

   b. Bay Bridge Series

c. Golden Gate Series

d. Pacific Ocean Series

14. Which player has NOT played for both the Oakland Athletics and the San Francisco Giants?

    a. Marco Scutaro

    b. Barry Zito

    c. Jason Giambi

    d. Miguel Tejada

15. Which player has NOT played for both the Oakland Athletics and the Los Angeles Angels?

    a. Bert Campaneris

    b. Dan Haren

    c. Carney Lansford

    d. Rich Harden

16. Before the Houston Astros moved to the division in 2013, the AL West was the only MLB division with four teams.

    a. True

    b. False

17. Which player has NOT played for both the Oakland Athletics and the Seattle Mariners?

    a. Ray Fosse

    b. Dwayne Murphy

    c. Dave Henderson

    d. Rick Honeycutt

18. Which player has not played for both the Oakland Athletics and the Texas Rangers?

a. Bert Campaneris
b. Jose Canseco
c. Dave Stewart
d. Eric Chavez

19. Which player has not played for both the Oakland Athletics and the Houston Astros?

a. Jed Lowrie
b. Miguel Tejada
c. Stephen Piscotty
d. Josh Reddick

20. When the A's play the Giants, it is often referred to as "The Battle of the Bay."

a. True
b. False

QUIZ ANSWERS

1. B – Kansas City Royals

2. A – True

3. B – Milwaukee Brewers

4. B – Oakland A's (17)

5. A – True

6. D – Oakland A's

7. A – True

8. A – 0

9. B – 1

10. A – 0

11. B – 1

12. B – False

13. B – Bay Bridge Series

14. C – Jason Giambi

15. D – Rich Harden

16. A- True

17. B – Dwayne Murphy

18. D – Eric Chavez

19. C – Stephen Piscotty

20. A – True

DID YOU KNOW?

1. The Oakland A's have the most American League West championships with 17 (as of the end of the 2020 season). The Los Angeles Angels have 9, the Texas Rangers have 7, and the Seattle Mariners and Houston Astros have 3 each. Teams formerly in the division that won AL West championships include the Kansas City Royals (6), Minnesota Twins (4), and Chicago White Sox (2). The most recent AL West Division champions are the Oakland A's (2020).

2. The AL West was founded in 1969 and included the Oakland A's, California Angels, Chicago White Sox, Kansas City Royals, Minnesota Twins, and Milwaukee Brewers (as the Seattle Pilots). Only the A's and Angels are still members of the AL West.

3. Currently, all AL West teams reside on the West Coast and in Texas. In the past, the American League West Division has had teams as far east as Chicago.

4. Since 2018, the Bay Bridge Series between the A's and Giants has had a trophy fashioned from a piece of the old Bay Bridge that collapsed during the 1989 World Series, in which the two teams faced each other.

5. The A's and Giants did not meet in regular season play until June of 1997 when interleague play began, even though the A's moved out to the Bay in 1968.

6. "The Big Three" were a group of three dominant A's pitchers in the early 2000s: Barry Zito, Tim Hudson, and Mark Mulder. Two of those three pitchers, Zito and Hudson, went on to play for the Giants.

7. Mike Aldrete, Kevin Appier, Andrew Bailey, Don Baylor, Joe Blanton, Orlando Cabrera, Alberto Callaspo, Bert Campaneris, Jesse Chavez, Bartolo Colon, David DeJesus, Dan Haren, Rickey Henderson, Jason Isringhausen, Reggie Jackson, Stan Javier, Scott Kazmir, Carney Lansford, Hideki Matsui, Dave Parker, Cliff Pennington, Tony Phillips, Joe Rudi, Huston Street, Don Sutton, and Kurt Suzuki have all played for both the Oakland Athletics and the Los Angeles Angels.

8. Yonder Alonso, Travis Blackley, Eric Byrnes, Ryan Cook, Jack Cust, Ray Fosse, Goose Gossage, Dave Henderson, Rickey Henderson, Rick Honeycutt, Stan Javier, Seth Smith, Dale Sveum, and Danny Valencia have all played for both the Oakland Athletics and the Seattle Mariners.

9. Elvis Andrus, Harold Baines, Travis Blackley, Milton Bradley, Bert Campaneris, Jose Canseco, Jesse Chavez, Bartolo Colon, Khris Davis, Justin Duchscherer, Goose Gossage, Rich Harden, Rick Honeycutt, Mitch Moreland, Matt Stairs, and Dave Stewart have all played for both the Oakland Athletics and the Texas Rangers.

10. Travis Blackley, Curt Blefary, Chris Carter, Octavio Dotel, Mike Fiers, Stan Javier, Scott Kazmir, Tony Kemp, Matt Keough, Jed Lowrie, Joe Morgan, Josh Reddick, Don

Sutton, and Miguel Tejada have all played for both the Oakland Athletics and the Houston Astros.

CHAPTER 15:

THE AWARDS SECTION

QUIZ TIME!

1. Which Oakland Athletics player won the American League MVP Award in 2000?

   a. Matt Stairs

   b. Eric Chavez

   c. Miguel Tejada

   d. Jason Giambi

2. Barry Zito won an American League Cy Young Award in 2002.

   a. True

   b. False

3. Which Oakland Athletics player was named the 2004 American League Rookie of the Year?

   a. Nick Swisher

   b. Bobby Crosby

   c. Huston Street

   d. Justin Duchscherer

4. Which Oakland Athletics player won a Gold Glove Award in 1981?

    a. Rickey Henderson
    b. Mike Norris
    c. Dwayne Murphy
    d. All of the above

5. Who is the only Oakland Athletics player to ever win a Platinum Glove Award?

    a. Josh Reddick
    b. Josh Donaldson
    c. Matt Chapman
    d. Eric Chavez

6. Which Oakland Athletics player won a Silver Slugger Award in 1991?

    a. Mark McGwire
    b. Rickey Henderson
    c. Jose Canseco
    d. Dave Henderson

7. No Oakland Athletics player has ever won the MLB Home Run Derby.

    a. True
    b. False

8. Which Oakland Athletics player was named the DHL Hometown Hero (voted by MLB fans as the most outstanding player in franchise history)?

a. Rickey Henderson

b. Dennis Eckersley

c. Reggie Jackson

d. Catfish Hunter

9. Who was the first Oakland Athletics player to win a Gold Glove Award?

a. Dwayne Murphy

b. Alfredo Griffin

c. Joe Rudi

d. Vic Power

10. Who was the first Oakland Athletics player to win a Silver Slugger Award?

a. Jason Giambi

b. Mark McGwire

c. Rickey Henderson

d. Jose Canseco

11. Billy Beane was named the _____ Baseball America Major League Executive of the Year.

a. 2002

b. 2006

c. 2012

d. 2015

12. Khris Davis won an Edgar Martinez Award in 2018.

a. True

b. False

13. Which two managers are the only Oakland Athletics managers to ever win the American League Manager of the Year Award?

    a. Connie Mack and Tony La Russa

    b. Billy Martin and Tony La Russa

    c. Tony La Russa and Bob Melvin

    d. Billy Martin and Bob Melvin

14. Which player won the 2013 Catfish Hunter Award?

    a. Coco Crisp

    b. Josh Donaldson

    c. Seth Smith

    d. Stephen Vogt

15. Which Oakland Athletics player won a Cy Young Award in 1971?

    a. Catfish Hunter

    b. Vida Blue

    c. Blue Moon Odom

    d. Rollie Fingers

16. No Oakland Athletics player has ever won a Roberto Clemente Award.

    a. True

    b. False

17. Which Oakland Athletics player was named the 1988 American League Rookie of the Year?

    a. Mark McGwire

    b. Stan Javier

c. Carney Lansford

d. Walt Weiss

18. How many Gold Glove Awards did Dwayne Murphy win during his time with the Oakland Athletics?

    a. 2

    b. 4

    c. 6

    d. 8

19. Which Oakland Athletics player won a Silver Slugger Award in 2002?

    a. David Justice

    b. Miguel Tejada

    c. Jermaine Dye

    d. Eric Chavez

20. Bob Melvin won the 2012 Chuck Tanner Major League Baseball Manager of the Year Award.

    a. True

    b. False

QUIZ ANSWERS

1. D – Jason Giambi

2. A – True

3. B – Bobby Crosby

4. D – All of the above

5. C – Matt Chapman

6. C – Jose Canseco

7. B – False (Mark McGwire, Yoenis Cespedes)

8. C – Reggie Jackson

9. D – Vic Power (1958)

10. C – Rickey Henderson (1981)

11. B – 2006

12. A- True

13. C – Tony La Russa and Bob Melvin

14. A – Coco Crisp

15. B – Vida Blue

16. B – False (Dave Stewart, 1990)

17. D – Walt Weiss

18. C – 6

19. D – Eric Chavez

20. A – True

DID YOU KNOW?

1. The Oakland Athletics have had five different players win Cy Young Awards: Vida Blue (1971), Catfish Hunter (1974), Bob Welch (1990), Dennis Eckersley (1992), and Barry Zito (2002).

2. The Oakland Athletics have had five different players win Silver Slugger Awards: Mark McGwire (1992, 1996), Jason Giambi (2001), Eric Chavez (2002), Rickey Henderson (1981, 1990), and Jose Canseco (1988, 1990, 1991).

3. The Oakland Athletics have had eight players named American League Rookie of the Year: Harry Byrd (1952), Jose Canseco (1986), Mark McGwire (1987), Walt Weiss (1988), Ben Grieve (1998), Bobby Crosby (2004), Huston Street (2005) and Andrew Bailey (2009).

4. The Oakland Athletics have had 11 different players win Gold Glove Awards: Mike Norris, Vic Power, Mark McGwire, Matt Olson, Eric Chavez, Matt Chapman, Alfredo Griffin, Joe Rudi, Dwayne Murphy, Rickey Henderson, and Josh Reddick.

5. The Athletics have had 12 players win American League MVP Awards: Eddie Collins (1914), Mickey Cochrane (1928), Lefty Grove (1931), Jimmie Foxx (1932, 1933), Bobby Shantz (1952), Vida Blue (1971), Reggie Jackson (1973), Jose Canseco (1988), Rickey Henderson (1990), Dennis

Eckersley (1992), Jason Giambi (2000), and Miguel Tejada (2002).

6. The Oakland Athletics have had three different players win the Edgar Martinez Award: Dave Kingman (1984), Dave Parker (1989), and Khris Davis (2018).

7. The Oakland Athletics have had four players win American League Comeback Player of the Year Awards: Matt Keough (1980), Dave Kingman (1984), Storm Davis (1988), and John Jaha (1999).

8. The Oakland Athletics have had two managers win American League Manager of the Year Awards: Tony La Russa (1988, 1992) and Bob Melvin (2012, 2018).

9. The Oakland Athletics have had four players win the Babe Ruth Award in the World Series: Gene Tenace (1972), Bert Campaneris (1973), Dick Green (1974), and Dave Stewart (1989).

10. The Oakland Athletics' Catfish Hunter Award is given annually to the A's player who best exemplifies Catfish's spirit. Winners so far include Tim Hudson (2004), Mark Ellis (2005, 2007), Jason Kendall (2006), Mike Sweeney (2008), Kurt Suzuki (2009), Ben Sheets (2010), Josh Willingham (2011), Jonny Gomes (2012), Coco Crisp (2013), Stephen Vogt (2014, 2015, 2016), Jed Lowrie (2017), Matt Chapman (2018), and Marcus Semien (2019, 2020).

CHAPTER 16:

THE TOWN

QUIZ TIME!

1. Oakland is the _____ largest city in the state of California.

   a. 3rd
   b. 7th
   c. 11th
   d. 15th

2. Oakland is the only city in the world that has a natural saltwater lake.

   a. True
   b. False

3. Oakland is home to more _____ per capita than any other city in the United States.

   a. bicyclists
   b. teachers
   c. chefs
   d. artists

4. Walt Disney got inspiration for Disneyland from _____, located in Oakland.

    a. The Oakland Zoo
    b. Jack London Square
    c. Children's Fairyland
    d. Oakland Museum of California

5. Which popular ice cream brand was founded in Oakland?

    a. Fentons
    b. Dreyer's
    c. Blue Bunny
    d. Both A and B

6. Which famous actor used to sell concessions at the Oakland Coliseum?

    a. Brad Pitt
    b. Tom Hanks
    c. Will Smith
    d. Johnny Depp

7. MC Hammer was once a batboy for the Oakland A's.

    a. True
    b. False

8. What is the name of the NFL team that was located in Oakland from 1960 through1980 and 1995 through 2019?

    a. Oakland Broncos
    b. Oakland Packers
    c. Oakland 49ers
    d. Oakland Raiders

9. What is the name of the NBA team that was located in Oakland from 1971 to 2019?

    a. Los Angeles Clippers
    b. Los Angeles Lakers
    c. Golden State Warriors
    d. Oakland SuperSonics

10. Where did the Oakland Raiders play during their time in Oakland?

    a. Oracle Arena
    b. Oakland Coliseum
    c. Chase Center
    d. Allegiant Stadium

11. Where did the Golden State Warriors play during their time in Oakland?

    a. Oracle Arena
    b. Oakland Coliseum
    c. Chase Center
    d. Allegiant Stadium

12. The Port of Oakland is responsible for 99% of goods moving through Northern California.

    a. True
    b. False

13. Which alcoholic drink was created in Oakland?

    a. Mojito
    b. Bloody Mary

   c. Old fashioned

   d. Mai tai

14. Oakland is home to the oldest bonsai tree in the United States.

   a. True

   b. False

15. Which of the following sweet treats was invented in Oakland?

   a. Cotton candy

   b. Popsicle

   c. S'mores

   d. Apple pie

16. Amelia Earhart's first solo flight was from Hawaii to Oakland.

   a. True

   b. False

17. Mrs. Fields first served her cookies at Oakland A's games.

   a. True

   b. False

18. What is Oakland International Airport's code?

   a. OIA

   b. OLD

   c. OAK

   d. OKD

19. Oakland is home to over _____ parks.

a. 40

b. 60

c. 80

d. 100

20. Lake Merritt was the first wildlife refuge in North America.

a. True

b. False

QUIZ ANSWERS

1. B – 7th

2. A - True

3. D – artists

4. C – Children's Fairyland

5. D – Both A and B

6. B – Tom Hanks

7. A- True

8. D – Oakland Raiders

9. C – Golden State Warriors

10. B – Oakland Coliseum

11. A – Oracle Arena

12. A- True

13. D – Mai Tai

14. A – True

15. B – Popsicle

16. A – True

17. A – True

18. C – OAK

19. C – 80

20. A – True

DID YOU KNOW?

1. Black olives were first canned in Oakland.

2. Rocky Road ice cream was created by William Dreyer and Joseph Edy in Oakland in 1929.

3. The window squeegee was created in Oakland in 1936.

4. The Bay Area slang word "hella" originated in Oakland around the 1970s.

5. There is a tiny, shrimp-like crustacean that is found only in Lake Merritt.

6. The Black Panther Party was founded in Oakland in 1966.

7. Bruce Lee opened a martial arts studio in Oakland in 1964.

8. The actor who plays Luke Skywalker in Star Wars, Mark Hamill, was born in Oakland.

9. Jonestown Cult leader, Jim Jones, is buried in Oakland along with over 400 of his followers.

10. Clint Eastwood attended high school in Oakland.

CHAPTER 17:

THE BASH BROTHERS

QUIZ TIME!

1. In his 16-season MLB career, Mark McGwire played for the Oakland A's and what other team?

    a. San Diego Padres

    b. Los Angeles Dodgers

    c. St. Louis Cardinals

    d. Montreal Expos

2. Jose Canseco's twin brother, Ozzie, also played in the MLB.

    a. True

    b. False

3. Where was Mark McGwire born?

    a. Long Beach, California

    b. San Diego, California

    c. Oakland, California

    d. Pomona, California

4. Where was Jose Canseco born?

a. Santo Domingo, Dominican Republic

b. Havana, Cuba

c. Santa Clara, Cuba

d. Punta Cana, Dominican Republic

5. Mark McGwire was named the 1987 American League Rookie of the Year.

a. True

b. False

6. How many Silver Slugger Awards did Mark McGwire win in his 16-season MLB career?

a. 1

b. 2

c. 3

d. 4

7. How many Silver Slugger Awards did Jose Canseco win in his 17-season MLB career?

a. 1

b. 2

c. 3

d. 4

8. Jose Canseco was named the 1986 American League Rookie of the Year.

a. True

b. False

9. How many MLB All-Star Games was Mark McGwire named to?

a. 10

b. 11

c. 12

d. 13

10. How many MLB All-Star Games was Jose Canseco named to?

a. 2

b. 4

c. 6

d. 8

11. Jose Canseco was named the _____ American League MVP.

a. 1987

b. 1988

c. 1989

d. 1990

12. Jose Canseco did NOT win a Gold Glove Award in his 17-season MLB career.

a. True

b. False

13. How many Gold Glove Awards did Mark McGwire win in his 16-season MLB career?

a. 1

b. 2

c. 3

d. 4

14. Mark McGwire attended the University of Southern California (USC).

    a. True

    b. False

15. How many World Series championships did Jose Canseco win?

    a. 1

    b. 2

    c. 3

    d. 4

16. How many World Series championships did Mark McGwire win in his 16-season MLB career?

    a. 1

    b. 2

    c. 3

    d. 4

17. Jose Canseco led MLB in RBIs in 1988.

    a. True

    b. False

18. How many times did Mark McGwire lead MLB in home runs?

    a. 1

    b. 3

    c. 5

    d. 7

19. How many times did Jose Canseco lead MLB in home runs?

    a. 1

    b. 2

    c. 3

    d. 4

20. Mark McGwire was named to the MLB All-Century Team.

    a. True

    b. False

QUIZ ANSWERS

1. C – St. Louis Cardinals

2. A – True

3. D – Pomona, California

4. B – Havana, Cuba

5. A – True

6. C – 3

7. D – 4

8. A – True

9. C – 12

10. C – 6

11. B – 1988

12. A – True

13. A – 1

14. A – True

15. B – 2 (1989 and 2000)

16. A – 1 (1989)

17. A – True

18. C – 5 (1987, 1996-1999)

19. B – 2 (1988 and 1991)

20. A – True

DID YOU KNOW?

1. In Jose Canseco's book, *Juiced: Wild Times, Rampant 'Roids, Smash Hits & How Baseball Got Big,* he claims that he and Bash Brother, Mark McGwire both used steroids during their MLB careers.

2. Mark McGwire hit 583 home runs during his MLB career and Jose Canseco hit 462 career home runs.

3. During his 17-season MLB career, Jose Canseco played for the A's, Texas Rangers, Tampa Bay Devil Rays, Boston Red Sox, New York Yankees, Chicago White Sox, and Toronto Blue Jays.

4. Due to their alleged use of performance-enhancing drugs (PEDs), neither Jose Canseco nor Mark McGwire has been inducted into the National Baseball Hall of Fame. Mark McGwire is a member of the Athletics Hall of Fame and the Cardinals Hall of Fame.

5. Mark McGwire was the St. Louis Cardinals' hitting coach from 2010-2012. He was the Los Angeles Dodger's hitting coach from 2013-2015. He was the San Diego Padres bench coach from 2016 to 2018.

6. Jose Canseco was the first player in MLB history to hit 30 home runs with four different teams (A's, Rangers, Blue Jays, and Rays). He was also the first MLB player to hit 40 home runs and steal 40 bases in the same season.

7. Mark McGwire's brother, Dan was an NFL quarterback for the Seattle Seahawks and Miami Dolphins. He was drafted in the first round of the NFL draft out of San Diego State University.

8. Mark McGwire voiced himself on a 1999 episode of *The Simpsons* entitled "Brother's Little Helper."

9. The Netflix special, *The Lonely Island Presents: The Unauthorized Bash Brothers Experience* featuring SNL alum, Andy Samberg is a visual rap album in which Andy Samberg plays Jose Canseco and Akiva Schaffer plays Mark McGwire.

10. In 1998, Mark McGwire set the MLB single-season home run record at 70. This record was broken three years later by Barry Bonds.

CHAPTER 18:

ROLLIE

QUIZ TIME!

1. What is Rollie Fingers' full name?

    a. a. George Roland Fingers
    b. b. Roland George Fingers
    c. c. Glen Roland Fingers
    d. d. Roland Glen Fingers

2. Rollie Fingers spent his entire 17-season MLB career with the Oakland Athletics.

    a. True
    b. False

3. What year was Rollie Fingers inducted into the National Baseball Hall of Fame?

    a. 1990
    b. 1991
    c. 1992
    d. 1993

4. How many Rolaids Relief Man of the Year Awards did Rollie Fingers win in his 17-season MLB career?

    a. 1
    b. 2
    c. 3
    d. 4

5. How many World Series championships did Rollie Fingers win during his 17-season MLB career?

    a. 1
    b. 2
    c. 3
    d. 5

6. How many MLB All-Star Games was Rollie Fingers named to?

    a. 4
    b. 5
    c. 6
    d. 7

7. Rollie Fingers was named the 1974 World Series MVP.

    a. True
    b. False

8. How many MVP Awards did Rollie Fingers win?

    a. 0
    b. 1
    c. 2
    d. 3

9. How many Cy Young Awards did Rollie Fingers win?

    a. 0
    b. 1
    c. 2
    d. 3

10. How many saves did Rollie Fingers collect?

    a. 321
    b. 331
    c. 341
    d. 351

11. What is Rollie Fingers' career ERA?

    a. 2.70
    b. 2.90
    c. 3.00
    d. 3.50

12. Rollie Fingers' uniform No. 34 is retired by both the Oakland A's and the Milwaukee Brewers.

    a. True
    b. False

13. How many times did Rollie Fingers lead the MLB in saves?

    a. 1
    b. 2
    c. 3
    d. 4

14. When was Rollie Fingers born?

    a. August 25, 1942
    b. August 25, 1946
    c. April 25, 1943
    d. April 25, 1948

15. How many strikeouts did Rollie Fingers collect?

    a. 999
    b. 1,099
    c. 1,299
    d. 1,499

16. Rollie Fingers pitched 1,701.1 innings.

    a. True
    b. False

17. Rollie Fingers is known for his _____.

    a. Mullet
    b. Handlebar mustache
    c. Two different-colored eyes
    d. Unibrow

18. Where was Rollie Fingers born?

    a. Kalamazoo, Michigan
    b. Marquette, Michigan
    c. Akron, Ohio
    d. Steubenville, Ohio

19. How many times was Rollie Fingers named the American League Player of the Week?

a. 1

b. 2

c. 4

d. 6

20. Rollie Fingers' career WAR is 25.6.

a. True

b. False

QUIZ ANSWERS

1. D – Roland Glen Fingers
2. B – False [He pitched for the A's (9 years), San Diego Padres (4 years), and Milwaukee Brewers (4 years)]
3. C – 1992
4. D – 4
5. C – 3
6. D – 7
7. A – True
8. B – 1 (1981)
9. B – 1 (1981)
10. C – 341
11. B – 2.90
12. A – True
13. C – 3 (1977, 1978, 1981)
14. B – August 25, 1946
15. C – 1,299
16. A – True
17. B – Handlebar mustache
18. D – Steubenville, Ohio
19. B – 2 (July 11, 1976, and August 8, 1976)
20. A – True

DID YOU KNOW?

1. When Rollie Fingers retired from professional baseball, he held the MLB record for career saves with 341. His record was broken by Jeff Reardon in 1992.

2. Rollie Fingers was only the second relief pitcher to be inducted into the National Baseball Hall of Fame.

3. Rollie Fingers is one of only ten players in MLB history to have their numbers retired by more than one MLB team.

4. Rollie Fingers and four members of his family appeared on a 1983 episode of the game show, *Family Feud*.

5. Rollie Fingers' mustache is mentioned by Homer Simpson when he is trying on different mustaches on an app on his tablet in an episode of *The Simpsons* titled "A Tree Grows in Springfield."

6. Rollie Fingers' mustache is ranked #1 in MLB history by Baseball Reference.com. He originally grew the mustache to get a $300 bonus from A's owner Charles Finley. He still rocks the handlebar to this day.

7. Rollie Fingers was inducted into the San Diego Hall of Champions in 2000.

8. In December 2020, one of Rollie Fingers' World Series championship rings was sold for $75,300 at an auction.

9. Rollie Fingers attended Chaffey College in Rancho Cucamonga, California.

10. Rollie Fingers made his MLB debut on September 15, 1968, vs. the Detroit Tigers at 22 years old. He played in his final MLB game on September 17, 1985, vs. the Baltimore Orioles at 39 years old.

CHAPTER 19:

AMERICA'S PASTIME

QUIZ TIME!

1. How many total teams play in Major League Baseball?

    a. 15
    b. 20
    c. 30
    d. 33

2. Major League Baseball was founded in 1903.

    a. True
    b. False

3. Who is the current commissioner of Major League Baseball?

    a. Bart Giamatti
    b. Fay Vincent
    c. Bud Selig
    d. Rob Manfred

4. What year was the National League founded?

a. 1870

b. 1876

c. 1903

d. 1911

5. What year was the American League founded?

    a. 1888

    b. 1901

    c. 1903

    d. 1918

6. Major League Baseball is the second wealthiest professional sports league. Which league is the wealthiest?

    a. NBA

    b. NHL

    c. NFL

    d. MLS

7. Major League Baseball headquarters is located in New York City.

    a. True

    b. False

8. How many games does each Major League Baseball team play per season?

    a. 92

    b. 122

    c. 162

    d. 192

9. In which two U.S. states is Major League Baseball's spring training held?

   a. California and Florida
   b. Arizona and Florida
   c. Arizona and California
   d. California and Arizona

10. How many stitches does an MLB baseball have?

   a. 98
   b. 100
   c. 108
   d. 110

11. Where is the National Baseball Hall of Fame located?

   a. Denver, Colorado
   b. Phoenix, Arizona
   c. Los Angeles, California
   d. Cooperstown, New York

12. All 30 Major League Baseball teams are located in the United States.

   a. True
   b. False

13. Which current MLB stadium is the oldest still in use?

   a. Angel Stadium
   b. Dodger Stadium
   c. Fenway Park
   d. Wrigley Field

14. Major League Baseball has the highest attendance of any sports league in the world.

   a. True
   b. False

15. Fill in the blank: Seventh Inning _____

   a. Jog
   b. Song
   c. Shake
   d. Stretch

16. William Howard Taft was the first United States president to throw out the ceremonial first pitch at a Major League Baseball game.

   a. True
   b. False

17. It is a Major League Baseball rule that all umpires must wear _____ underwear in case they rip their pants.

   a. Tan
   b. Gray
   c. White
   d. Black

18. What year did the first World Series take place?

   a. 1903
   b. 1905
   c. 1915
   d. 1920

19. Former Major League Baseball Commissioner Bart Giamatti is the father of actor, Paul Giamatti.

    a. True
    b. False

20. The song traditionally played in the middle of the seventh inning at Major League Baseball games is called *Take Me Out to the Ballpark.*

    a. True
    b. False

QUIZ ANSWERS

1. C – 30

2. A - True

3. D – Rob Manfred

4. B – 1876

5. B – 1901

6. C – NFL

7. A- True

8. C – 162

9. B – Arizona and Florida

10. C – 108

11. D – Cooperstown, New York

12. B – False, 29 out of 30 (The Toronto Blue Jays are located in Canada)

13. C – Fenway Park

14. A – True

15. D – Stretch

16. A – True

17. D – Black

18. A - 1903

19. A – True

20. B – False (*Take Me Out to the Ballgame*)

DID YOU KNOW?

1. The average lifespan of a baseball in a Major League Baseball game is five to seven pitches. This means that approximately five to six dozen baseballs are used in every game.

2. The Boston Americans won the very first World Series. They defeated the Pittsburgh Pirates in eight games. Today the most games a World Series can go is seven.

3. The New York Yankees currently hold the most World Series titles in Major League Baseball with 27 (as of the end of the 2020 MLB season).

4. Hot dogs are the most popular food item sold at Major League Baseball ballparks. Over 21 million hot dogs were sold at MLB stadiums in 2014.

5. The longest Major League Baseball game on record was played on May 9, 1984, between the Chicago White Sox and Milwaukee Brewers. The game lasted 8 hours, 6 minutes. The most innings played in a Major League Baseball game was 26 on May 1, 1920, in a game between the Brooklyn Dodgers and Boston Braves.

6. The mound to home plate distance at Major League Baseball ballparks is 60 feet, 6 inches.

7. Before it can be used in a Major League Baseball game, each baseball is rubbed with special mud to improve grip

and reduce luster. This special mud comes from a specific, secret location in the state of New Jersey.

8. The fastest Major League Baseball game on record took place on September 28, 1919. The game between the New York Giants and Philadelphia Phillies took 51 minutes. An average MLB game is 3 hours.

9. The American League uses a designated hitter. A DH only hits and does not play in the field. In the National League, the pitcher hits instead of there being a designated hitter. If an interleague game is being played, whether a DH is used or not is determined by which team is the home team. If the home team is from the American League, each team will use a DH. If the home team is from the National League, each team's pitcher will hit.

10. The distance between bases in Major League Baseball is 90 feet.

CHAPTER 20:

GOATS

QUIZ TIME!

1. How many World Series championships did Babe Ruth win during his 22-season career?

    a. 3
    b. 5
    c. 7
    d. 9

2. Jackie Robinson's uniform No. 42 was retired by ALL MLB teams in 1997.

    a. True
    b. False

3. How many MLB All-Star Games was Willie Mays named to during his 22-season MLB career?

    a. 8
    b. 14
    c. 20
    d. 24

4. How many National League Batting Titles did Tony Gwynn win in his 20-season MLB career?

   a. 2
   b. 6
   c. 8
   d. 10

5. Rickey Henderson holds the all-time MLB record for most stolen bases. How many did Rickey steal during his 25-season MLB career?

   a. 1,306
   b. 1,406
   c. 1,506
   d. 1,606

6. What year was Hank Aaron inducted into the National Baseball Hall of Fame?

   a. 1980
   b. 1981
   c. 1982
   d. 1983

7. Derek Jeter was named the 1996 American League Rookie of the Year.

   a. True
   b. False

8. How many Gold Glove Awards did Ken Griffey Jr. win in his 22-season MLB career?

a. 7

b. 8

c. 9

d. 10

9. How many no-hitters did Nolan Ryan throw in his 27-season MLB career?

   a. 1

   b. 3

   c. 7

   d. 9

10. Ted Williams missed what season due to military service?

    a. 1943

    b. 1944

    c. 1945

    d. All of the above

11. How many times was Joe DiMaggio named MVP during his 13-season career?

    a. 0

    b. 1

    c. 2

    d. 3

12. Stan Musial spent his entire 22-season MLB career with the St. Louis Cardinals.

    a. True

    b. False

13. What year was Reggie Jackson inducted into the National Baseball Hall of Fame?

    a. 1990
    b. 1993
    c. 1995
    d. 1999

14. Cal Ripken Jr. spent his entire 21-season MLB career with the Baltimore Orioles.

    a. True
    b. False

15. How many MLB All-Star Games was Roberto Clemente named to in his 18-season MLB career?

    a. 5
    b. 10
    c. 15
    d. 18

16. Johnny Bench spent his entire 17-season MLB career with the Cincinnati Reds.

    a. True
    b. False

17. How many ERA Titles did Sandy Koufax win during his 12-season MLB career?

    a. 2
    b. 3
    c. 4
    d. 5

18. Frank Robinson was named the _____ National League Rookie of the Year.

    a. 1955

    b. 1956

    c. 1965

    d. 1966

19. Lou Gehrig spent his entire 17-season career with the New York Yankees.

    a. True

    b. False

20. Rod Carew was named the 1967 American League Rookie of the Year.

    a. True

    b. False

QUIZ ANSWERS

1. C – 7

2. A - True

3. D – 24

4. C – 8

5. B – 1,406

6. C – 1982

7. A- True

8. D – 10

9. C – 7

10. D – All of the above

11. D – 3

12. A -True

13. B – 1993

14. A – True

15. C – 15

16. A – True

17. D – 5

18. B – 1956

19. A – True

20. A – True

DID YOU KNOW?

1. Babe Ruth spent his 22-season career with the New York Yankees, Boston Red Sox, and Boston Braves. He is a member of the National Baseball Hall of Fame, MVP, 2x MLB All-Star, 7x World Series champion, batting title champion, and ERA title winner. Ruth is often regarded as the greatest baseball player of all time.

2. Jackie Robinson spent his entire 10-season career with the Brooklyn Dodgers. He is a member of the National Baseball Hall of Fame, MVP, 6x MLB All-Star, 1955 World Series champion, batting title champion, and 1947 National League Rookie of the Year. Robinson is best known for breaking the color barrier in baseball.

3. Willie Mays spent his 22-season career with the San Francisco Giants and New York Mets. He is a member of the National Baseball Hall of Fame, 2x MVP, 1951 National League Rookie of the Year, 24x MLB All-Star, 1954 World Series champion, 12x Gold Glove Award winner, batting title champion, 2x MLB All-Star Game MVP, and Major League Player of the Year.

4. Tony Gwynn spent his entire 20-season career with the San Diego Padres. He is a member of the National Baseball Hall of Fame, 15x MLB All-Star, 5x Gold Glove Award winner, 7x Silver Slugger Award winner, and 8x batting title champion.

5. Rickey Henderson spent his 25-season career with the Oakland A's, New York Yankees, San Diego Padres, New York Mets, Boston Red Sox, Los Angeles Dodgers, Anaheim Angels, Seattle Mariners, and Toronto Blue Jays. He is a member of the National Baseball Hall of Fame, MVP, 2x MLB All-Star, 7x World Series champion, and batting title champion. Henderson is often regarded as the greatest leadoff hitter of all time. He holds the MLB record for most stolen bases.

6. Hank Aaron spent his 23-season career with the Atlanta Braves and Milwaukee Brewers. He is a member of the National Baseball Hall of Fame, MVP, 25x MLB All-Star, 1957 World Series champion, 2x batting title champion, and 3x Gold Glove Award winner.

7. Derek Jeter spent his entire 20-season career with the New York Yankees. He is a member of the National Baseball Hall of Fame, 14x MLB All-Star, 1996 American League Rookie of the Year, 5x World Series champion, World Series MVP, MLB All-Star Game MVP, 5x Gold Glove Award winner, and 5x Silver Slugger Award winner.

8. Stan Musial spent his entire 22-season career with the St. Louis Cardinals. He is a member of the National Baseball Hall of Fame, 3x MVP, 24x MLB All-Star, 3x World Series champion, 7x batting title champion, and 2x Major League Player of the Year.

9. Cal Ripken Jr. spent his entire 21-season career with the Baltimore Orioles. He is a member of the National

Baseball Hall of Fame, 2x MVP, 19x MLB All-Star, 1982 American League Rookie of the Year, 1983 World Series champion, 2x Gold Glove Award winner, 8x Silver Slugger Award winner, 2x MLB All-Star Game MVP, and 2x Major League Player of the Year.

10. Sandy Koufax spent his entire 12-season career with the Los Angeles/Brooklyn Dodgers. He is a member of the National Baseball Hall of Fame, MVP, 3x Cy Young Award winner, 3x Triple Crown winner, 7x MLB All-Star, 3x World Series champion, 2x World Series MVP, 5x ERA title winner, and 2x Major League Player of the Year.

CONCLUSION

Learn anything new? Now you truly are the ultimate A's fan! Not only did you learn about the Green and Gold of the modern era, but you also expanded your knowledge back to the early days of the franchise.

You learned about the Oakland Athletics' origins and their history, plus how far they've come. You learned about the history of their uniforms and jersey numbers and read some of the craziest nicknames of all time. You learned more about the GOAT, Rickey Henderson. You also learned about Hall of Famers Dennis Eckersley and Rollie Fingers. Plus, who could forget about the Bash Brothers? You were amazed by A's stats and recalled some of the most infamous A's trades and drafts/draft picks of all time. You broke down your knowledge by outfielders, infielders, pitchers, and catchers. You looked back on the A's playoff feats and the awards that came before, after, and during them. You also learned about the A's fiercest rivalries, both within their division and outside it.

Every team in the MLB has a storied history, but the Oakland Athletics have one of the most memorable of all. They have gone through winning seasons and losing seasons with the backing of their devoted fans. Being the ultimate A's fan takes knowledge and a whole lot of patience, which you tested with this book. Whether you knew every answer or were stumped by several questions, you learned some of the most interesting history that the game of baseball has to offer.

The deep history of the Oakland Athletics franchise represents what we all love about the game of baseball. The heart, the determination, the tough times, and the unexpected moments, plus the players that inspire us and encourage us to do our best because, even if you get knocked down, there is always another game and another day.

With players like Matt Chapman, Matt Olson, and Ramón Laureano, the future for the Oakland Athletics continues to look bright. They have a lot to prove but there is no doubt that this franchise will continue to be one of the most competitive teams in Major League Baseball year after year.

It's a new decade, which means there is a clean slate, ready to continue writing the history of the Oakland Athletics. The ultimate A's fan cannot wait to see what's to come for their beloved boys in Green and Gold.

Made in the USA
Las Vegas, NV
30 January 2024

85120712R00098